Wiring Circuits

Also available

Beginner's Guide to Electric Wiring (3rd edition)
Electric Wiring: Domestic (8th edition)
Electrical Contracting (2nd edition)
Electrical Installation Technology (3rd edition)
Modern Wiring Practice (9th edition)
Newnes Electrical Pocket Book (18th edition)

Wiring Circuits

Michael Neidle FIElecIE, TEng(CEI), ASEE(Dipl)
Associate Member of the Institution of Electrical Engineers

Heinemann : London

Heinemann Professional Publishing Ltd
22 Bedford Square, London WC1B 3HH

LONDON MELBOURNE JOHANNESBURG AUCKLAND

First published by Butterworth & Co. (Publishers) Ltd 1951
Second edition 1959
Third edition 1970
Fourth edition 1985
First published by William Heinemann Ltd 1986
Reprinted 1987

British Library Cataloguing in Publication Data

Neidle, Michael
    Wiring circuits.—4th ed.
    1. Electric wiring, Interior
    I. Title
    621.319′24   TK3271

ISBN 0 434 91435 5

Printed in England by Whitstable Litho Printers Ltd., Whitstable, Kent

Preface

Today, electrical contractors and installation and maintenance engineers and electricians undertake a variety of work ranging from installation of high-voltage distribution systems in large industrial plants to the wiring of domestic premises. They are also concerned with the electrical and electronic equipment used in the operation of many industrial machines and processes.

For practical engineers and electricians, only a basic knowledge of technological theory is needed to enable them to carry out installation and maintenance work efficiently. Their principal interest is in knowing how the various units of an installation are connected together in order to meet the specific requirements of the installation, and in having sufficient information to enable them to locate defective wiring and faults in units of equipment and components.

The wiring circuits presented in this book are intended to convey the kind of information that practical technicians require to help them with their work. Many of the diagrams illustrate the detailed circuits of various installations. Some are block diagrams simply showing the basic connections of units of complex installations which, utilizing specialized units, necessarily involve wiring circuits designed for the particular installation.

This fourth edition is in line with the 15th Edition of the IEE *Regulations for Electrical Installations*. All material has been thoroughly revised, but to assist maintenance engineers certain circuits still in common use have been retained. A chapter on energy management has been added as a guide for engineers concerned with reducing energy costs.

M.N.

Contents

Acknowledgements

Grateful acknowledgement is given for their assistance to the following companies:

AMF/Venner International Ltd.
Chloride Standby Systems Ltd.
Conrad & Ridout Ltd.
Cortina Electric Co Ltd.
Danfloss Ltd.
Electrocomp Ltd.
Electronic Control Systems Ltd.
Elkay Electrical Manufacturing Ltd.
Findlay, Durham & Brodie Ltd.
W. J. Furse Ltd.
Chloride Gent Ltd.
GEC Machines Ltd.
GEC Rectifiers Ltd.
GKN Lincoln Electric Ltd.

Holec Ltd.
Home Automation Ltd.
Lansing Industrial Robots Ltd.
MK Electric Ltd.
Myson Ltd.
Neco Electronics (Europe) Ltd.
Ottermill Ltd.
Satchwell Sunvic Ltd.
Smiths Industries Ltd.
Square D Ltd.
Safety Technology Ltd.
Renold Power Transmission Ltd.
Thorn Ltd.
MTE Ltd.
Landis & Gyr Ltd.

1 Distribution systems

Most consumers in the United Kingdom receive an electricity supply derived from a high voltage three-phase 50 Hz distribution system. Industrial consumers with heavy load demands are given a supply at a high voltage that is either used for a works distribution system with step-down transformer substations at different points, or is stepped down in one main substation feeding a low voltage distribution system.

Supply voltages

For the largest industrial plants, the incoming supply may be derived from a local transmission system operating at, say, 33 kV or 66 kV, and is stepped down to a lower high voltage for the works distribution system. In some cases, the distribution system voltage of, say, 6.6 kV or 11 kV is used directly for high voltage motors and equipment, or is stepped down to about 3.3 kV.

The low voltage (e.g. 415 V) supply is derived from the star-connected secondary winding of the step-down transformers and it may be distributed by either a three-wire system (Fig. 1.1) or a four-wire system (Fig. 1.2). With the three-wire system the voltage is the same between any two phases so that it can be used to supply both three-phase and single-phase equipment at the same voltage. With the four-wire system the voltage between one phase and neutral is that produced by one phase of the

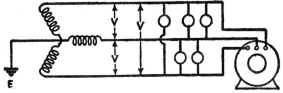

Fig. 1.1. Three-phase three-wire a.c. distribution

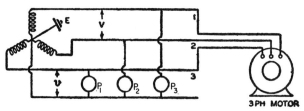

Fig. 1.2. Three-phase four-wire a.c. distribution

transformer secondary winding so that the phase voltage equals $\sqrt{3}$ times the phase-to-neutral voltage. Therefore, with the standard low voltage of 415 V between phases, the phase-to-neutral voltage is $415/\sqrt{3} = 240$ V.

In general, the three-wire system is used only to supply three-phase loads while the four-wire system provides both for 415 V three-phase loads and 240 V single-phase loads. A four-wire 415/240 V supply is given to premises where there is a requirement for three-phase equipment or where the demand is high enough to necessitate the introduction of the 415 V system into the consumer's premises. In the interests of safety, this is avoided when possible and the supply is given by a 240 V phase-and-neutral cable.

Low voltage (l.v.) is defined as voltages corresponding to 50–600 V a.c. between conductors and earth or 50–1000 V a.c. between conductors, or for 120–900 V d.c. between conductors and earth or 120–1500 V d.c. between conductors.

Voltages above l.v. are considered high voltage. Extra-low voltages (e.l.v.) are those not above 50 V a.c. or 120 V d.c.

To enable electricity to be used safely and efficiently, a distribution system must be planned and installed in accordance with whatever statutory regulations apply to the use of electricity in the premises involved, and it should also meet the requirements of the current edition of the Regulations for Electrical Installations issued by The Institution of Electrical Engineers. These Regulations are accepted as the authoritative guide to the design and engineering of electrical installations. (Throughout this book, the installation requirements discussed are those of the 15th Edition, in force at the time of publication.)

Industrial distribution systems

A typical arrangement of a distribution system for a large industrial plant is shown in Fig. 1.3. The high-voltage switchboard could be supplied from the ring-main 11 kV feeders forming part of the network of the local electricity authority; or it could be located in one substation of a number supplied from a ring main providing an 11 kV distribution system around the plant. In the latter case the 11 kV supply would be derived from a main substation stepping down from 33 kV, 66 kV or 132 kV (assuming that the plant is located in the United Kingdom). The magnitude of the load demand would determine from which system the incoming supply would be provided.

With the arrangement shown in Fig. 1.3, each of the transformers would have a capacity of, say, 1000 kVA. The h.v. switchboard forms part of a ring main system with one circuit-breaker controlling the incoming supply and the other the outgoing supply. A bus-section circuit-breaker is normally closed but would be opened, together with the appropriate feeder circuit-breaker to isolate a transformer from the h.v. system.

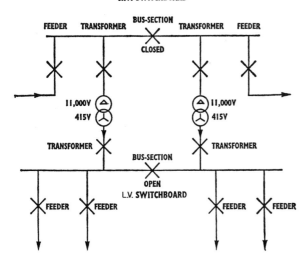

Fig. 1.3. Distribution system for a large industrial plant

Low-voltage circuit-breakers control the output from each transformer and each of the four feeders, and the l.v. switchboard includes a bus-section circuit-breaker that is normally open to limit the short-circuit current in the event of a fault on the l.v. system. When the total load is such that it can be carried by one transformer, the bus-section circuit-breaker is closed and one transformer is switched out.

In many industrial plants the load is such that only one substation is needed and this may contain only one transformer. Similarly, only one transformer may be installed in each of the substations fed from a works high-voltage ring main. The arrangement of the system depends on whether it is imperative to maintain continuously a supply to all parts of an industrial plant. If this is the case, then a complicated distribution system is necessary.

Fig. 1.4 shows a system designed to ensure the availability of a works supply in all circumstances except the complete loss of the incoming supply. Distribution is by a h.v. ring main with automatic circuit-breakers to provide for switching sections as required in the event of faults or the need to carry out maintenance. With appropriate fault protection schemes the system can be operated as a closed ring main so that in the event of a cable fault the section involved is disconnected at each end without loss of supply.

Alternatively, the system can be operated as an open ring main, with simpler fault protection. The ring main would be opened at a point where each out-going feeder would be equally loaded. A cable fault would interrupt the supply to certain substations but after the operation of the appropriate circuit-breakers to isolate the faulty section, supply would be restored by closing the circuit-breaker that is normally open to divide the ring main. As a further safeguard there are three transformers in each substation and if necessary the l.v. supply to a particular l.v. switchboard can be maintained by an interconnection with the l.v. switchboard in another substation. This interconnection also permits all the h.v. switchgear and transformers in a substation to be isolated for maintenance while the supply is still available from the l.v. switchboard.

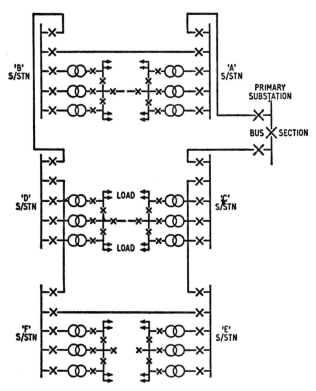

Fig. 1.4. Industrial distribution system arranged to ensure continuity of supply

Every circuit requires a circuit protective conductor (c.p.c.) connected to the consumer's main earthing terminal adjacent to the consumer's terminals. This provision also applies to all outlet points including lighting circuits which must have a c.p.c. run to all switch and light outlets. To enable them to be connected to the protective conductor, an earth terminal must be provided in all insulated switch boxes and also in metal switch boxes where there is not a solid conduit connection to the box and cover plate.

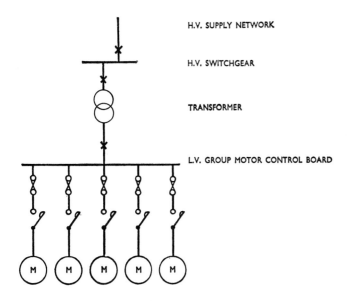

Fig. 1.5. Main three-phase circuits from the busbars of a group motor control board serving as final circuits to large motors

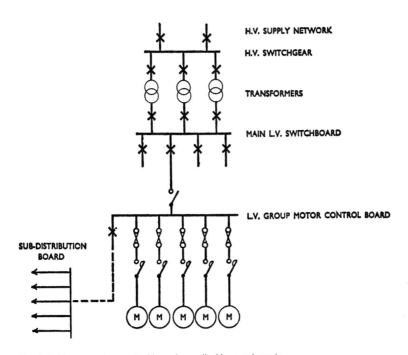

Fig. 1.6. Group motor control board supplied by a sub-main

Low-voltage distribution circuits

In industrial distribution systems three-wire and four-wire circuits supply three-phase and single-phase low-voltage power to the production plant. These circuits may be used to feed main distribution boards; or as sub-mains to sub-distribution boards supplying two or more final circuits; or as final circuits.

In practice, some main three-phase circuits may serve as final circuits supplying large motors or other individual loads (Fig. 1.5) or, as shown in Fig. 1.6, a sub-main may supply a group motor control board when this is a convenient unit to provide centralized starting and control facilities for motors that operate together to power a production process. It is a particularly suitable unit when motors have to be started in a certain sequence and must all be shut down if one fails. To provide a supply for lighting and other equipment in the area used for the production process, a sub-distribution board can be connected to the busbars of the group motor control board.

For the single-phase supplies, the arrangement shown in Fig. 1.7 can be used; protective conductors are omitted for clarity. The broken line represents that part of the system where the main l.v. switchboard is located. From the three-phase four-wire board, the single-phase circuits are taken to switch-fuse boards each feeding a distribution fuseboard. This is known as the TN-S supply system. T stands for earth and N for neutral, while S denotes that the protective (earth) and neutral conductors are separate.

It will be noted that *when the neutral point of a supply, or one pole of a transformer on the consumer's premises is earthed permanently, it is not permissible to have a fuse, non-linked switch or circuit-breaker in the line connected to earth.*

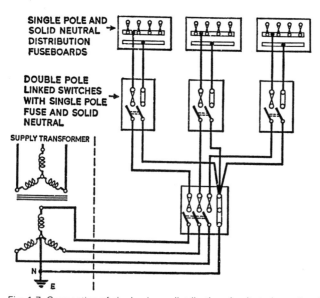

SINGLE POLE AND SOLID NEUTRAL DISTRIBUTION FUSEBOARDS

DOUBLE POLE LINKED SWITCHES WITH SINGLE POLE FUSE AND SOLID NEUTRAL

SUPPLY TRANSFORMER

N

E

Fig. 1.7. Connection of single-phase distribution circuits to incoming three-phase supply

Other supply systems

Fig. 1.8 shows a TT system (in this and following figures a single-phase supply is shown for clarity). The TT method is largely employed in country areas with overhead transmission lines. From Fig. 1.8 it will be seen that in contrast to the TN-S system there is no metallic path from the sub-station secondary winding's star point to the consumer's terminals. Because the

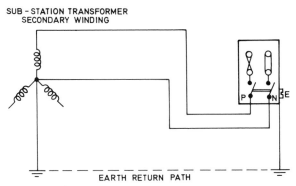

Fig. 1.8. TT system

earth path may be of a high resistance, a residual current circuit-breaker (r.c.c.b.) is often fitted. However, for protection against indirect contact in domestic premises, every socket-outlet requires a residual current circuit-breaker with a maximum rated current of 30 mA.

There is no earth return in the IT system (Fig. 1.9). Here, I stands for 'isolated from earth', although an impedance may be introduced. Due to the omission of an earth return path there are severe limitations to this system. Under the Electricity Supply Regulations 1937 this system must not be connected to a public supply.

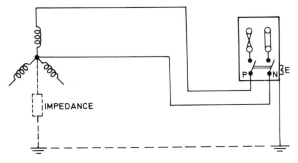

Fig. 1.9. IT system

The combined neutral and earth of the TN-C system (Fig. 1.10) is called a PEN conductor and it may be continued right through the consumer's installation with the use of earth concentric wiring usually by means of mineral-insulated copper-sheathed cable (m.i.c.c.). The copper sheath acts as the combined earth/neutral conductor.

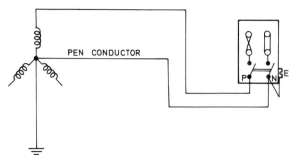

Fig. 1.10. TN–C/TN–C–S system

In the TN-C-S system the PEN conductor, sometimes referred to as a combined neutral and earth (CNE) conductor, is also employed, but conventional separate phase and neutral conductors are fitted for the internal wiring, i.e. the phase and neutral conductors are kept quite separate. Both TN-C and TN-C-S systems lend themselves to the protective multiple earthing (PME) type of transmission.

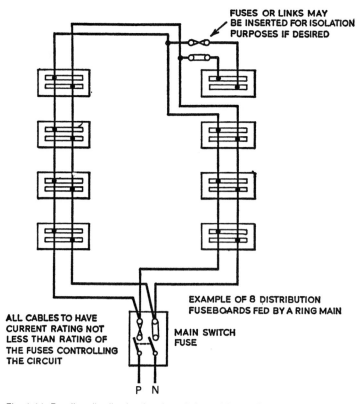

Fig. 1.11. Feeding distribution fuseboards by a rising main

Distribution fuseboards

A sub-main may be used as a ring main feeding several distribution boards. A similar arrangement controlled by a single-phase main switch-fuse is shown in Fig. 1.11. The sub-main can also form a circuit looping to the busbars of several distribution boards. With both these arrangements a line fuse and a neutral link may be inserted in the connections from the sub-main to the distribution board (Fig. 1.11). The insertion of fuses and links is recommended as a good practice as they enable the board to be isolated from the rest of the circuit.

For industrial and commercial premises which do not require a three-phase supply, a typical single-phase distribution system would be that shown in Fig. 1.12. The particular arrangement of the system from the consumer's switch-fuse depends on the load and the services that have to be supplied. The layout of the premises determines the location of the

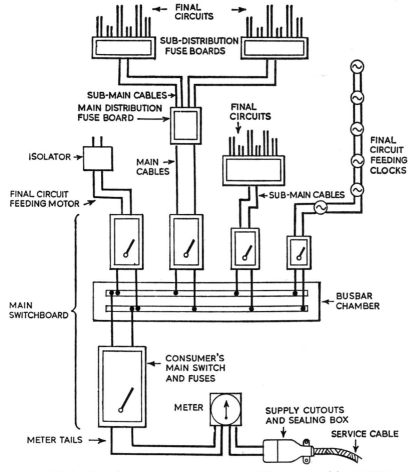

Fig. 1.12. Single-phase distribution system for an industrial or commercial consumer

distribution boards and the capacity and number of ways of each board depend on what the circuits supply.

Various arrangements of boards and circuits are shown in Figs. 1.13 and 1.14. The diagrams illustrate methods of connecting distribution fuse-boards which are permitted by the IEE Wiring Regulations. The basic requirement is that every distribution fuseboard must be connected to and controlled by the main switch-fuse, or by a separate way on a larger distribution fuseboard or switchboard, or by a circuit feeding several boards, as in Fig. 1.11.

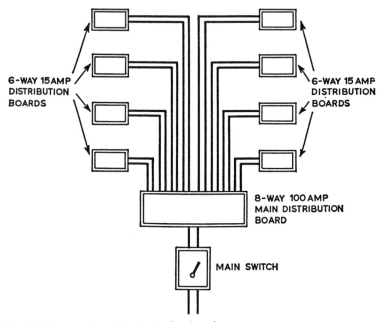

6-WAY 15AMP
DISTRIBUTION
BOARDS

6-WAY 15 AMP
DISTRIBUTION
BOARDS

8-WAY 100 AMP
MAIN DISTRIBUTION
BOARD

MAIN SWITCH

Fig. 1.13. Connection of distribution fuseboards

The permissible methods of connecting final circuits are shown in Fig 1.14. In industrial and commercial installations the circuits will be grouped for specific loads so that, for example, there are four groups supplying respectively: equipment units with a rated capacity below 15 A, units with a rated capacity above 15 A, an extensive lighting system and a large motor or other unit of a rated capacity that necessitates a direct connection to a main switch and not simply to one way of a sub-distribution fuseboard.

Ring circuits

Based on the ring main system (Fig. 1.4) in industrial and commercial premises, a final circuit in the form of a ring circuit may be used with advantage. Although 13 A socket-outlets and fused plugs are standard for domestic installations in the United Kingdom, the system is not restricted to such installations.

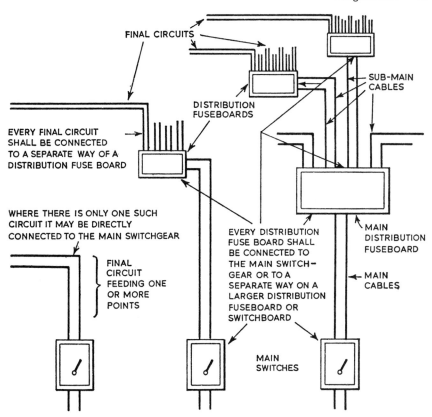

FINAL CIRCUITS

SUB-MAIN
CABLES

DISTRIBUTION
FUSEBOARDS

EVERY FINAL CIRCUIT
SHALL BE CONNECTED
TO A SEPARATE WAY OF A
DISTRIBUTION FUSE BOARD

WHERE THERE IS ONLY ONE SUCH
CIRCUIT IT MAY BE DIRECTLY
CONNECTED TO THE MAIN SWITCHGEAR

EVERY DISTRIBUTION
FUSE BOARD SHALL
BE CONNECTED TO
THE MAIN SWITCH-
GEAR OR TO A
SEPARATE WAY ON A
LARGER DISTRIBUTION
FUSEBOARD OR
SWITCHBOARD

MAIN
DISTRIBUTION
FUSEBOARD

FINAL
CIRCUIT
FEEDING ONE
OR MORE
POINTS

MAIN
CABLES

MAIN
SWITCHES

Fig. 1.14. Permissible methods for connecting final circuits

A ring circuit (Fig. 1.15) consists of an earth wire and two current carrying conductors looped from one socket-outlet to another, both ends of the circuit being connected to the phase and neutral terminals of a single fuse or circuit breaker. It is permissible to cut the conductors where they loop into the terminals of socket-outlets provided that the continuity of the ring circuit is maintained by satisfactory joints. An unlimited number of socket-outlets are permitted for a floor area not exceeding $100\,\text{m}^2$ but the following considerations must be taken into account. For domestic installations the load concentration in kitchens may demand wiring by a separate ring circuit. Separate circuits are also required for immersion heaters supplying tanks with a capacity in excess of 15 litres, or permanently connected heating appliances forming part of a space-heating installation.

A saving in cable can often be made by using spur circuits connected into the ring circuit, as shown in Fig. 1.15. Each non-fused spur must not feed more than one single or one twin socket-outlet or one permanently connected piece of equipment. The total number of fused spurs is unlimited but the number of non-fused spurs must not exceed the socket-outlets and stationary equipment connected to the circuit. Fixed

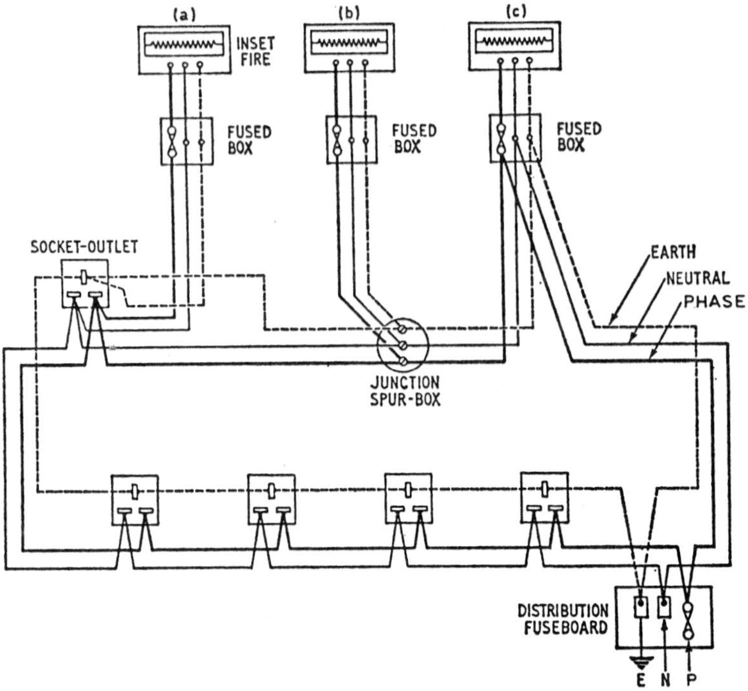

Fig. 1.15. Typical ring circuit for 13 A accessories. Three methods of connecting a fixed appliance to a ring-circuit using fused spur boxes: (a) wiring from socket-outlet terminals to fused connector box; (b) inserting a junction box in the ring-circuit conductors and wiring to fused connector box; (c) looping ring-circuit conductors into fused connector box

appliances may also be connected to a ring circuit provided they are protected by local fuses or miniature circuit-breakers with ratings not exceeding 13 A and 15 A respectively. Such appliances are usually connected by means of a switched and fused connector having a front flexible cable outlet.

13 A sockets and plugs may be fitted to a radial circuit, also allowing an unlimited number of points provided the looping of socket-outlets is either wired by 4 mm^2 p.v.c. or 2.5 mm^2 m.i.c.c. cable within a floor area of 50 m^2 and protected by 30 A or 32 A cartridge fuses or circuit-breakers, or wired by 2.5 mm^2 p.v.c. or 1.5 mm^2 m.i.c.c. cable within a floor area of 20 m^2 and protected by 20 A fuses or circuit-breakers.

Domestic distribution systems

A ring circuit is included in the domestic distribution system shown in Fig. 1.16. The single-phase supply to the installation is through a consumer's supply control unit which, in this case, includes the supply fuse, meter, consumer's main switch, the fuseways for all the services and the neutral bar. Because the unit meets specified requirements of the IEE Wiring Regulations, the consumer's main fuse is omitted, overall protection being given by the supply authority's fuse.

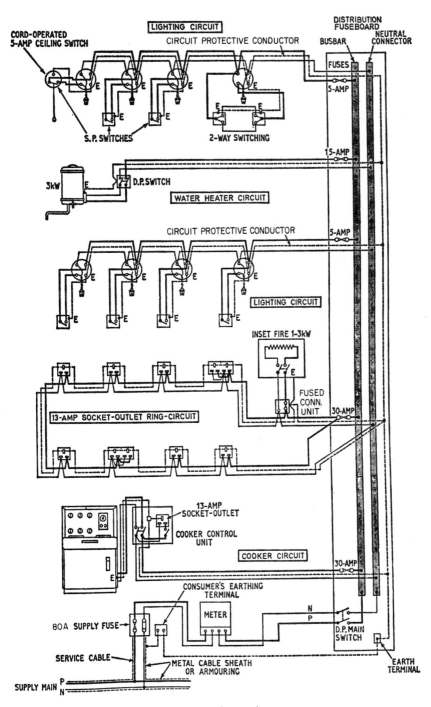

Fig. 1.16. Domestic wiring with circuit protective conductors

When a consumer's control unit is not used, the incoming supply will be controlled by the consumer's main switchgear, which may consist of a switchfuse or a separate switch and fuses.

As shown in Fig. 1.17, the switchgear must be fitted as close as possible to the supply authority's meter and service fuses so that the tails connecting the meter to the switchgear are as short as possible. The tails have to be provided by the consumer's contractor as near as possible to the meter.

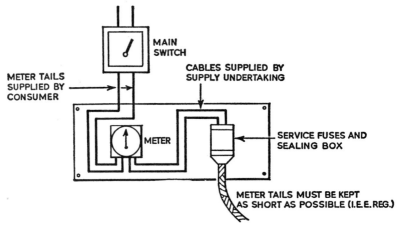

Fig. 1.17. Arrangement of consumer's main switch, meter and incoming service cable

For small installations, a splitter unit (Fig. 1.18) can provide both the main switch and the distribution fuseboard which has developed into the modern consumer's control unit, thus reducing the cost of the installation.

Because joints must be minimized when installing p.v.c. cable in conduit, the looping-in system is adopted. It should be noted that this does not imply that one length of cable is bared at intervals and looped-in at

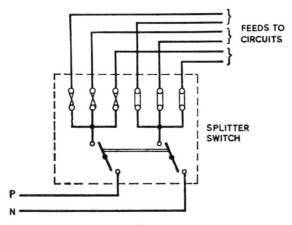

Fig. 1.18. Splitter unit for small installations

switch and lighting terminals. In practice, the two lengths of cable forming the loop are threaded in separately and the junction is made at the switch, light or other terminal. The arrangement of cables in a typical conduit lighting installation is shown in Fig. 1.19.

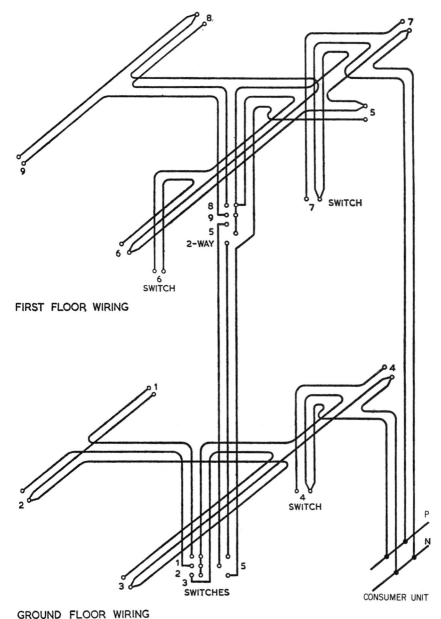

Fig. 1.19. Arrangement of cables in a typical conduit installation

D.C. distribution systems

Although few consumers in the United Kingdom now receive a d.c. supply, various industries still use direct current extensively for variable-speed motors and processing work. In general, however, these requirements are met not from a public d.c. system but from equipment installed and operated by the consumer and designed to give special-purpose supplies. The circuits for these equipments are described in Chapter 3.

In areas where the supply authority maintains a d.c. distribution system this will usually be a three-wire system as shown in Fig. 1.20. The supply voltage is in the range 200/400 V to 240/480 V, the lower voltage being between one outer and the middle wire and the higher voltage between the two outers.

When the higher voltage is required, the consumer receives a three-wire supply arranged as shown in Fig. 1.21. For domestic and other low demand

Fig. 1.20. Three-wire d.c. distribution

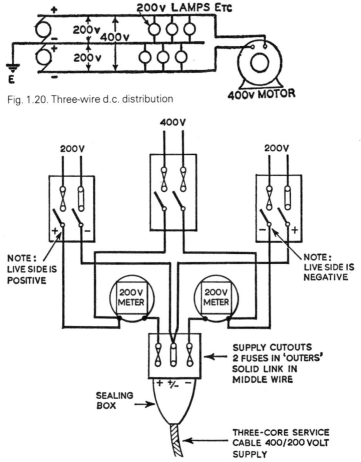

Fig. 1.21. Connections to provide two-wire distribution circuits from an incoming three-wire d.c. supply

installations, a supply is given by a two-wire service cable between one outer and the middle wire. If the outer is positive then the live side will be positive, but if the outer is negative then the live side will be negative. This must be taken into account when connecting up battery charging or other equipment which depends on correct polarity, and it must not be assumed that the earthed middle wire is negative.

It must also be ensured that all accessories used are intended for use on d.c. systems since many present-day accessories are not suitable for d.c.

2 Protective schemes

To protect distribution systems against the effects of short-circuits, these must be interrupted rapidly by the operation of relays and automatic circuit-breakers or by high rupturing capacity fuses. Any electrical installation must include an effective earthing system to ensure operation of the devices intended to interrupt currents flowing from a phase conductor to the metallic enclosures of equipment and cables.

As in the United Kingdom all these metallic enclosures have to be bonded together and connected effectively to earth, a short-circuit current from a line to earthed metal flows back through the earth to the source of supply, as shown in Fig. 2.1. The protection against this type of fault is

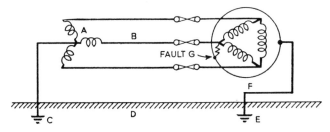

Fig. 2.1. Illustrating the earth-fault path in a typical circuit

therefore known as earth-fault or earth-leakage protection. However, it should be noted that both these terms are applied sometimes to any form of protection against phase-to-earth faults but are also used to distinguish between schemes applicable to different classes of circuit. There is really no clear distinction between the two forms of protection but usually it may be considered that earth-fault protection is used for high voltage units and circuits and low-voltage transformer secondary windings and feeders. An earth-fault protective scheme is intended to operate at high speed at relatively low values of fault current, to initiate the opening of circuit-breakers that disconnect the faulty circuit from the rest of the system. The scheme must also discriminate between the unhealthy and the healthy circuits so that the latter are not disconnected, thus ensuring the minimum disturbance to the system. The speed of disconnection is such that there is no dangerous rise of potential of metallic enclosures of equipment and cables, and the minimum of damage to equipment and cables.

In general, it may be considered that earth-leakage protection is used for consumers' low-voltage circuits to initiate the opening of a circuit-breaker to disconnect the supply to a large section of, or to the whole of, the installation. The primary function of earth-leakage protection is to prevent the persistence of an earth-fault current that would cause earthed metallic enclosures to be made alive at a lethal voltage. At the same time, the persistent earth-leakage current could also cause heating and sparking which might start a fire.

An earth-fault current may persist when with a fuse-protected system the impedance of the earth path restricts the current to a value that will not blow the fuse. As the fuse is only intended to blow with a current exceeding the normal load of the circuit, it follows that it will not blow if the earth-fault current is less than the normal load current, which can be the case if the earth-path impedance is high enough. As shown in Fig. 2.1, if an earth fault develops on the consumer's side of line B, the current is determined by the impedance of the loop circuit comprising line B, the transformer winding, the transformer earth connection, the path through the earth, and the consumer's earth connection. The critical section of the loop is the earth return path C-G, which largely determines the total impedance of the phase-earth loop.

To avoid the dangerous consequences of persistent earth leakage due to fault currents being restricted by the loop impedance, the IEE Wiring Regulations require earth-leakage circuit-breakers to be used instead of fuses when the loop impedance is such that the earth-fault current will not blow the fuse. This requirement also applies to prohibit the use of excess-current circuit-breakers which will not trip with the maximum earth-fault current available.

Main earthing system

Earth-fault protection operates to disconnect an unhealthy section from the rest of the system and also prevents all the metallic enclosures of electrical equipment and cables rising to a potential dangerous to life. For the earth-fault protection to operate, there must be a continuous path between the fault and the earth connection of the transformer or alternator capable of carrying the fault current without the risk of damaging healthy equipment and cables.

Considering a typical industrial step-down transformer substation, the star-points of the secondary windings must be properly earthed together with all the metal frames of the equipment and the neutral of a four-wire system. In general all the earth connections are made to a substation main earth bar which is connected to the substation earth electrode system. The earth bar is supported on a wall by insulators and, as shown in Fig. 2.2, the transformer neutral earthing insulated cables and the equipment frame earthing bare cables are brought separately to the bar. One main earthing insulated cable is taken to the substation earth electrode system.

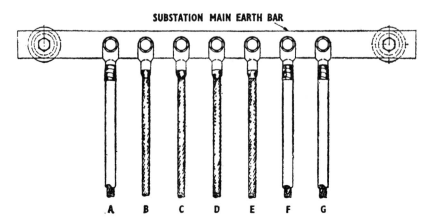

Fig. 2.2. Substation earthing connections:
A   Insulated conductor to substation earth electrode
B   Bare-stranded conductor to h.v. switchgear frame earth
C   Bare-stranded conductor to switchgear frame earth
D   Bare-stranded conductor to transformer No. 1 frame earth
E   Bare-stranded conductor to transformer No. 2 frame earth
F   Insulated conductor to transformer No. 1 neutral earth
G   Insulated conductor to transformer No. 2 neutral earth

As the earthing system may have to carry up to several thousand amperes, according to the system short-circuit capacity, for the time it takes for the protection to operate, all earthing cables and electrodes must be able to carry this current without a dangerous temperature rise or voltage gradient along the earthing system.

The transformer neutral earthing cables must be insulated because they will be earthed only at one point, at the main earth bar. Where a transformer neutral is brought out from a transformer as one core of a multi-core cable, and run direct to a switchboard or a fuseboard, the board neutral bar should be insulated from the board frame, and the incoming neutral cable connected to this bar. A separate insulated cable is used to join the neutral bar to the substation main earth bar.

If the incoming neutral cable is connected to a neutral bar which is not insulated from the board frame, this would not cause any trouble while the board frame remained properly earthed. However, if there is a deterioration or a break in the system connecting the board frame, the substation main earth bar and the earth electrode, the board frame potential to earth would rise to the same value as that of the now unearthed, or poorly earthed, transformer neutral, which may be a dangerous condition.

Earthing of consumer installations

For effective earth-fault protection of all consumer low voltage installations all metal parts which have to be earthed, in accordance with the IEE Wiring Regulations, must be connected to a protective conductor which is connected by means of an earthing lead to the earth electrode. The protective conductor can be a metal trunking system, cable armouring or sheathing, metal conduit, or an independent conductor. It is essential for all conducting metalwork to be bonded across possible gaps or high resistance joints to ensure that the impedance of the continuity circuit is minimized.

The earthing system may be a copper strip or rod, supplemented by connecting the earth lead to sheathing or armouring of underground cable laid directly in the ground, or any other conducting object which is in effective contact with the earth. In certain areas with overhead distribution, the supply authority may provide an earthing conductor; and in other areas a protective multiple earthing (PME) system may be used, in which case the neutral of the supply serves as an earth electrode at the consumer's installation.

All a.c. circuits must be protected by a control device that operates to interrupt the circuit in the event of excessive overload, or a phase-to-phase or a phase-to-earth short-circuit. Operation of the control device, other than a fuse, will involve the use of a protective trip integral with the device, or an arrangement of apparatus forming a protective scheme.

Factors determining protective scheme

The scheme adopted depends on several factors, such as the circuit voltage and the maximum current that can flow when a short-circuit occurs, and the degree of continuity of supply required. The protective requirements for each distribution system must be examined individually but the scheme selected will generally be one from a particular class of schemes which are similar in principle.

The main factor determining the class of scheme adopted is the possible maximum value of fault current. Because of the vast difference in possible fault current, an 11 kV feeder of a distribution network will require an automatic circuit-breaker and discriminating relays whereas a fused plug suffices for a domestic appliance.

D.C. circuits are protected by fuses or circuit-breakers with tripping devices sensitive to excess current and in some cases reverse current. Special protective schemes used with d.c. motors and other equipment are described in the relevant chapters.

Considering main distribution systems involving the use of switchgear up to 11 kV and 350 MVA breaking capacity, the protection requirements are relatively simple. In general, all circuits have to be protected against excessive currents, in the form of overloads, short-circuits or earth faults. Basically, the protective scheme required to interrupt the flow of excessive current consists of a device which, on sensing the abnormal conditions, initiates the opening of a circuit-breaker; or alternatively, the heating effect of the current results in the melting of a fuse-link.

Direct-acting overload trips

The most elementary device for initiating the opening of a circuit-breaker is the direct-acting series-connected overload trip in the form of an electro-magnet and armature or a solenoid and plunger. The coil of the tripping device consists of a few turns of conductor connected in series with the main circuit and acting on the armature or the plunger which is linked with the circuit-breaker mechanism. The d.c. circuit-breaker in the connection diagram shown in Fig. 2.3 has a direct-acting series trip.

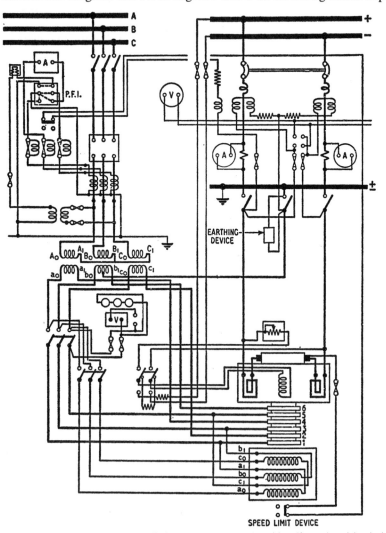

Fig. 2.3. Protective schemes applied to a rotary converter with self-synchronizing induction motor starting. On the a.c. side the circuit-breaker is tripped under fault conditions by trip coils shunted by time-lag fuses and energized from current transformers. The d.c. circuit-breaker is tripped on overload by a direct-acting series trip and on reverse current by a voltage-current operated device

Instead of being operated by means of a series-connected coil, the direct-acting overload trip device can be operated via a current transformer (Fig. 2.3). This method has advantages where it is necessary to insulate the trip device from the main circuit. Also, since a current transformer can be designed to saturate at predetermined overcurrent values, it is possible to obtain overload settings that are lower than those obtainable with a series-connected coil.

Use of time-limit fuses

With current transformer operation, a time-limit fuse can be used to obtain a time lag on overloads (Figs. 2.3 and 2.6). The fuse is connected across the trip coil and, consequently, the overload trip device is prevented from operating until the fuse melts due to a current in excess of its rating. The thermal characteristic of the fuse provides a satisfactory time lag for overload currents. The operation of these tripping devices from current transformers also permits these to be used for earth-leakage protection, when connected in parallel.

Although the time-limit fuse gives a time lag which initially decreases as the overload current increases, with short-circuit currents the fuse blows almost instantaneously so that if fused trips were used for the circuits both to and from a substation, a short-circuit on an outgoing circuit could trip out an incoming circuit. Hence, this form of protection is not acceptable for major circuits of a system.

Methods of obtaining discriminative tripping

When a short-circuit occurs on an outgoing feeder from the busbars of a substation, the fault current tends to operate all the devices protecting the various sections of the system through which it flows. Referring to Fig. 2.4, A is a circuit-breaker on the secondary side of a transformer connected to busbars with outgoing feeders B, C, and D. Assuming a fault on feeder D in the position shown, the fault current will flow through both circuit-breakers A and D and will therefore tend to operate the protective devices on both. It is required that D should trip while A remains closed to supply the two healthy feeders. To this end it is necessary to use a protective scheme which ensures that circuit-breaker D trips out before A. One method is to use protective devices with time delays which, in the case being considered, are adjusted so that D trips in a shorter time than A.

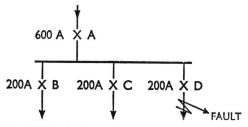

Fig. 2.4. Discriminative tripping of two circuit-breakers in series; normal full load currents are indicated

When a succession of tripping devices are adjusted to operate in different times with the same fault current, so that only the one nearest to the fault actually trips, the protective scheme is classified as time-graded. A correctly time-graded scheme will give discriminative tripping.

To obtain discriminative tripping with the system represented in Fig. 2.4, a direct-acting trip coil fitted to circuit-breaker A must be capable of giving a designed time delay for fault currents of any magnitude up to the full short-circuit value. Time-lag fuses do not give sufficient delay under short-circuit conditions to permit discriminative tripping; but other time delay devices for use with direct-acting trip coils are designed specifically to produce a delay under all conditions. These devices have a definite minimum time characteristic, i.e. although the time delay decreases with increasing values of current, under maximum fault conditions there is still a definite minimum time delay before the trip operates.

For major systems where a succession of circuit-breakers is to be controlled by a time-graded protective scheme, this would involve the use of inverse definite minimum time (IDMT) relays set to provide a difference in tripping time of approximately 0.4 second between adjacent circuit-breakers under short-circuit conditions.

The objection to time-graded protection is that it imposes maximum delay in tripping adjacent to the power source where it is likely that the fault current will be a maximum. Considering the system shown in Fig. 2.5 a time-graded scheme using IDMT relays could be used to obtain correct discriminative tripping between circuit-breakers A, B and C. However, with this scheme the delay in tripping becomes progressively longer as the power source is approached. Circuit-breaker A would have the longest time delay and C the least although the consequences of a prolonged flow of fault current at A are likely to be more serious that at C – even assuming that the relay at A is operating in its minimum time.

If the supply circuit includes appreciable impedance, a fault adjacent to the power source would result in a considerably larger fault current than would a fault at the remote end of a feeder. In this case it may be practicable, if the difference in fault current would be large enough, to fit an instantaneous tripping device adjacent to the power source which would operate only with faults close to the source. This instantaneous device would enable heavy faults near the power source to be cleared without waiting for an IDMT relay to operate.

With the system represented in Fig. 2.5, the transformer introduces a considerable amount of impedance. Taking into account only the

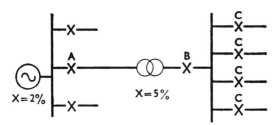

Fig. 2.5. Discriminative tripping by current grading

reactances of the system, that of the power source, referred to the transformer kVA rating, is given as 2 per cent, and that of the transformer as 5 per cent. If it is assumed that the cable reactance is negligible, a fault on the primary terminals of the transformer would result in a fault current of $100/2 = 50$ times full load current; and on the secondary terminals, a fault current of $100/(2 + 5) = 14.3$ times normal full load.

If then an instantaneous tripping device is fitted to circuit-breaker A and set to operate at, say, a current equivalent to 20 times normal full load, it would operate in the event of a short-circuit occurring at any point between the transformer primary terminals and circuit-breaker A. A fault on the secondary terminals of the transformer, or on any part of the circuit connected to those terminals, cannot operate the instantaneous relay and would be cleared by the time-graded protection.

Many industrial main distribution systems can be protected effectively by an IDMT relay scheme with perhaps fused direct-acting trips for the final circuit-breakers of end sections of a radial system, or an open ring-main system.

Connections for protective schemes using either fused direct-acting trips or IDMT relays are shown in Figs. 2.6 and 2.7. With the latter scheme the circuit-breaker is opened by a shunt trip coil the circuit of which includes an auxiliary switch that is closed when the circuit-breaker closes. The trip circuit is then ready to be closed in the event of a fault current causing the relay to operate to close its trip contacts. The supply for the shunt trip is obtained from the d.c. bus wires which are fed from a battery.

It will be noted that with the schemes shown in Figs 2.6 and 2.7, two of the direct-acting and two of the relay operating coils are connected so that they are energized with phase-to-phase faults and, in each case, the third coil is connected in parallel with the three current transformers (as shown in Fig. 2.8(b)) and is therefore sensitive to earth-fault currents.

Earth-fault protection schemes

Since many electrical faults are initially between one phase and earth, it is advantageous to use a protective scheme including a direct-acting trip coil or a relay that is sensitive to the flow of earth-fault current.

Fig. 2.8(a) shows the simple method of detecting earth-fault currents, known as core-balance protection. If the system is healthy, no current can flow from any of the supply connections to earth, in which case all current flowing into the load must return via the three phase connections. It follows that the sum of the currents in the three lines is zero under normal conditions, and the sum of the magnetomotive forces due to the currents is also zero. Consequently, no flux would be induced in an annular ring of laminations embracing the three lines. If a leakage to earth develops some of the current flowing into the load will return via an earth path instead of by the lines so that the sum of the currents in the three lines is no longer zero. In this circumstance, a flux is induced in the ring and a voltage is induced in the coil, causing a current to flow and operate the earth-fault relay.

26

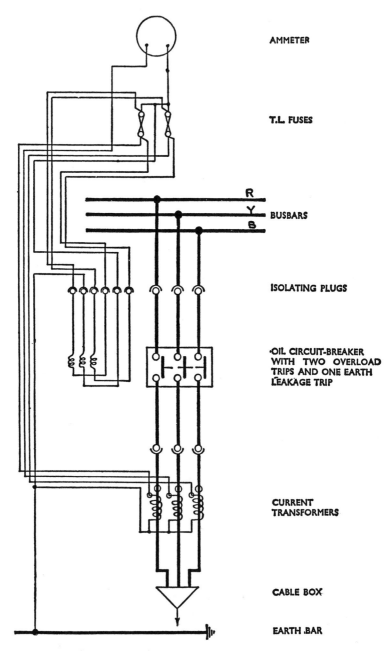

AMMETER

T.L. FUSES

R
Y BUSBARS
B

ISOLATING PLUGS

·OIL CIRCUIT-BREAKER
WITH TWO OVERLOAD
TRIPS AND ONE EARTH
LEAKAGE TRIP

CURRENT
TRANSFORMERS

CABLE BOX

EARTH .BAR

Fig. 2.6. Protective scheme using two fused overload trips and one earth-leakage trip

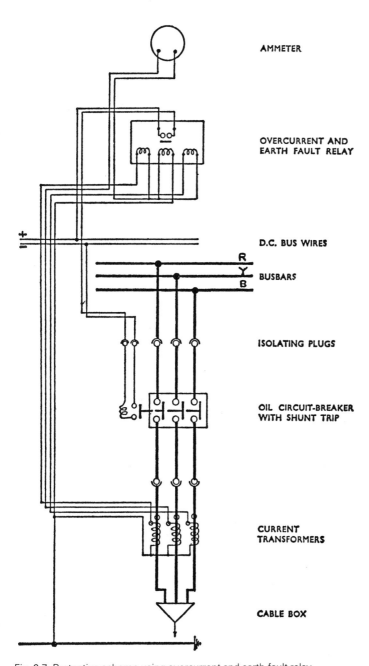

AMMETER

OVERCURRENT AND
EARTH FAULT RELAY

D.C. BUS WIRES

R
Y BUSBARS
B

ISOLATING PLUGS

OIL CIRCUIT-BREAKER
WITH SHUNT TRIP

CURRENT
TRANSFORMERS

CABLE BOX

Fig. 2.7. Protective scheme using overcurrent and earth-fault relay

Similar results are achieved by using three residually connected current transformers, as shown in Fig. 2.8(*b*). Under healthy conditions the sum of the currents produced by the current transformer secondaries is zero and no current flows through the relay.

It is important to note the variations in the protected zone due to different current transformer connections used to energize the earth-fault relay or trip coil operating to open the circuit-breaker.

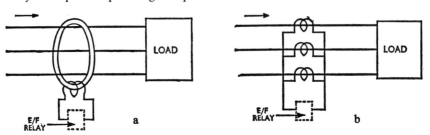

Fig. 2.8. (a) Core-balance earth-fault protection. (b) Residually connected current transformers for earth-fault protection

Fig. 2.9 shows a solidly earthed star winding, which could represent either an alternator or a transformer winding. A relay connected to a single current transformer in the earth connection (position A) would operate in the event of an earth fault occurring anywhere on the circuit, including the alternator or transformer winding, since any earth-fault current, whatever its origin, must flow through the neutral current transformers.

If however a relay is supplied from three residually connected current transformers (position B), this relay would not operate with a fault on the star winding since, in this case, the fault current would not flow through any of the three current transformers. Both relays shown in Fig. 2.9 are 'unrestricted' in operation, i.e. they will operate with a fault anywhere on the external system.

Fig. 2.10 shows 'restricted' earth-fault protection as applied to a star winding. The relay operates with a fault on the star winding but does not

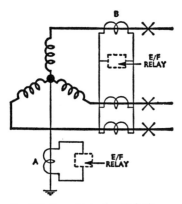

Fig. 2.9. Unrestricted earth-fault protection

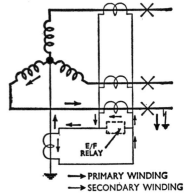

Fig. 2.10. Restricted earth-fault protection of a star winding

operate with a fault on the external system, i.e. the protected zone is restricted to the star winding. A fault to earth is shown on the external system and it will be noted that the affected phase current transformer and the neutral current transformer produce equal and opposite currents so that a circulating current is established between them and no current flows through the relay.

Earth-fault protection on three-phase four-wire systems introduces slight complications. With core-balance protection the four cores of the cable required for the system must be enclosed within the annular ring since, with current flowing in the neutral, it is the sum of four currents that is zero.

The scheme shown in Fig. 2.8(b) can be adapted for use on a four-wire system by adding a fourth current transformer, the primary being inserted in the neutral cable core and the secondary winding being connected in parallel with the existing three secondaries. Connections would be similar to those shown in Fig. 2.12. With this arrangement of four current transformers, a fault between one phase and neutral has exactly the same effect as a fault between two phases; two current transformers are energized and produce equal and opposite secondary currents which sum to zero. Consequently, the relay is not energized, being sensitive only to a true earth fault, i.e. a current flow between a phase line and earth. These arrangements are unrestricted in operation. It should be noted that the simplest form of unrestricted earth-fault protection is provided by a single current transformer in the earth connection.

Restricted earth-fault protection in a three-phase four-wire system may be required for a star-connected winding. One of two schemes can be used according to the position of the earth connection in the main circuit.

Consider a transformer winding supplying a four-wire system as shown in Fig. 2.11. Two connections are taken to the transformer neutral: one to earth and one to the neutral busbar. Such an arrangement may be dictated by cabling requirements. In these circumstances five current transformers are required; the circuit and operation being similar to the protective scheme shown in Fig. 2.10 for a three-wire system using four current transformers. The fifth current transformer is required in the neutral

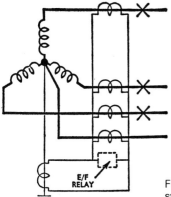

E/F
RELAY

Fig. 2.11. Restricted earth-fault protection on a four-wire system using five current transformers

connection in order that single-phase loads may produce currents in the secondary circuit which sum to zero like the currents of a three-phase load.

Where the earth connection can be made, not direct to the neutral terminal of the power transformer, but to a point on the neutral lead which is on the load side of the neutral current transformer, then a total of four current transformers can provide restricted earth-fault protection. To satisfy this condition, the earth connection could be made to the neutral busbar, as shown in Fig. 2.12. This also shows the primary and secondary currents resulting from a phase-to-earth fault outside the protected zone. It will be seen that two current transformers produce equal and opposite currents with consequent non-operation of the relay. Similarly, a three-phase or single-phase fault (or load current) cannot operate the relay.

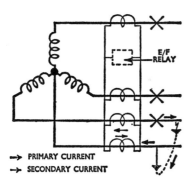

→ PRIMARY CURRENT
→ SECONDARY CURRENT

Fig. 2.12. Restricted earth-fault protection on a four-wire system using four current transformers (showing an earth fault outside the protected zone)

In the event of a fault developing between a winding of the power transformer and earth (or on the connections between the transformer terminals and the current transformers) the fault current flows to earth, returning to the transformer neutral via the earth connection and the neutral current transformer. The latter is the only current transformer energized; consequently the relay will operate.

Restricted earth-fault protection does not necessarily imply that four current transformers are required. Three residually connected current transformers provide restricted earth-fault protection to a three-phase delta winding, which has no earth connection. Irrespective of circuit conditions, the sum of the currents flowing in and out of a delta winding must be zero unless there is a breakdown of insulation that provides a connection to earth for the flow of fault current.

Earth-fault relays can be time-graded in the same way as overcurrent relays and both relays can be combined with voltage elements so that they operate to trip associated circuit-breakers only when power is flowing in the opposite direction to the normal flow. These directional overcurrent and earth-fault relays are usually applied under two basic circumstances.

They can be used firstly for either transformers or feeders which operate in parallel where the normal power flow is always in a forward direction but may reverse under fault conditions; and secondly, for closed ring-main systems with time-graded protection.

Fig. 2.13 shows a typical ring-main circuit to which directional protection has been applied to all substations with the exception of the primary, where it is unnecessary since power flow can be in one direction only, namely out to the ring. Such a system may be regarded as two

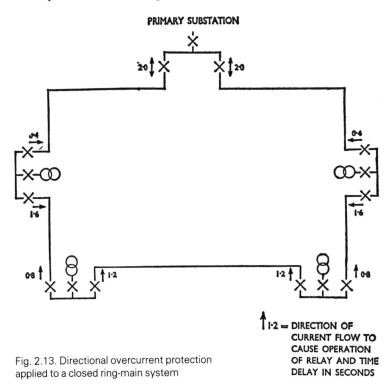

Fig. 2.13. Directional overcurrent protection applied to a closed ring-main system

↑ 1·2 = DIRECTION OF CURRENT FLOW TO CAUSE OPERATION OF RELAY AND TIME DELAY IN SECONDS

superimposed radial feeders so time-graded that fault power fed from either end of the ring results in the tripping of the circuit-breaker nearest to the fault. Thus a fault anywhere on the ring-main trips the two circuit-breakers on either side of it due to one relay operating on overcurrent and a second relay operating on directional overcurrent.

The directional relay consists of an IDMT overcurrent element controlled by a directional element. With a current flow in one predetermined direction, the directional element does not operate and consequently the overcurrent element cannot operate. When current flows in the reverse direction, the directional element operates to complete a circuit which enables the over-current element to operate and close its trip contacts to open the circuit-breaker.

For the protection of major distribution systems where it is essential to avoid the disconnection of healthy circuits, time-graded schemes are not acceptable and it is necessary to use some form of circulating current or differential scheme which, with a fault in the protected zone, trips the circuit-breaker as quickly as possible.

Circulating current protection

Applied to the protection of alternators and power transformers, circulating current or differential schemes ensure that there is no risk of the alternator or transformer circuit-breakers being tripped except with an internal fault, i.e. the schemes are completely stable with faults external to the protected zone.

Fig. 2.14 shows the application of circulating current protection to an alternator. In effect, each phase of the winding is protected separately. Under healthy conditions the current flowing into the winding must equal the current flowing out, so that a circulating current is established between the two current transformers and there is no voltage across the relay to cause it to operate. A phase-to-phase fault on the windings or an earth fault will unbalance the currents so that the relay is energized. An inter-turn fault on one phase does not unbalance the currents entering and leaving the winding, consequently the relay does not operate with such a fault.

With a circulating current scheme applied to an alternator, as the current transformers are arranged to balance in pairs per phase, it is not as difficult to achieve stability as with earth-fault schemes. However, certain complications arise when this form of protection is applied to power transformers since these may introduce a phase shift between primary and secondary windings which can vary with different connections. Any such phase shift must be compensated for by suitable current transformer arrangements.

For example, referring to Fig. 2.15 showing typical connections for a delta-star power transformer, with this there is a phase shift of 30° between primary and secondary. Compensation is made by connecting the current transformers on the delta side in star, and connecting those on the star side in delta. In order that the currents from the two groups of current transformers may have the same magnitude, the ratios differ. If the star-connected current transformer has a rating of 5 A, then the delta-connected current transformers would be rated at $5/\sqrt{3} = 2.89$ A.

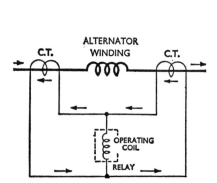

Fig. 2.14. Connections for circulating current protection of one phase of an alternator

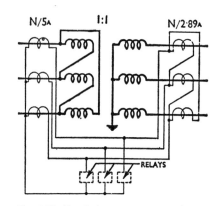

Fig. 2.15. Circulating current protection of a delta-star transformer

A further difficulty with transformer protection is due to the fact that when the transformer primary winding is switched on to the supply, the transient magnetizing current surge has no counterpart in the secondary winding. Consequently, spill currents flow into the relays and tend to operate them. The normal method of ensuring stability during the switching surge is to provide a time delay on the relay.

For complete stability under either healthy or through-fault conditions, it is necessary to have identical outputs from each group of current transformers. When power transformers are fitted with tap-changers it is impossible for the current transformers to remain matched at all tap positions. With power transformers having a large ratio, it is also difficult to arrange for the current transformers on the primary side to match up with those on the secondary side in order to give identical outputs both in phase and magnitude.

The difficulties encountered due to tap-changing and inequalities in current transformers can be overcome by applying a system of bias through the relay, as shown in Fig. 2.16. It will be seen that in addition to the relay

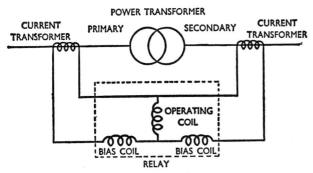

Fig. 2.16. Biased differential protection for a power transformer

operating coil there are also bias coils which apply increasing restraint to the relay with increasing through-fault currents or normal unbalanced currents in the current transformer closed circuit. With an internal fault, the difference between the outputs of the two current transformers is sufficient to allow the operating coil to overcome the restraining effect of the bias coils.

Protection by h.r.c. fusegear

With certain classes of industrial low-voltage distribution system, effective and discriminating protection is achieved by using high rupturing capacity (h.r.c.) fusegear instead of automatic circuit-breakers and relays or trips. For normal load circuit switching some form of switch is used in conjunction with the fuses. Switches and fuses may be combined in fuse-switch or switch-fuse units. The difference between these units is demonstrated in Fig. 2.17. The fuse-switch incorporates cartridge fuse-links bolted or clamped directly on to the moving contact assembly of

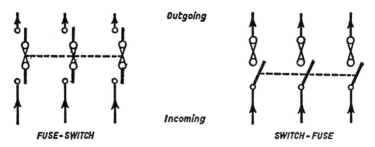

Fig. 2.17. Difference between fuse-switch and switch-fuse units

a switch. With the switch-fuse unit the switch and the fuses are separate, and the fuses may be h.r.c. cartridge or semi-enclosed types.

Both types of unit are designed to provide for circuit isolation; the switching of overload currents; protection against overload and short-circuit currents; and the safe closure of the switch on to a short-circuit, which will be cleared by the operation of the fuses.

Fig. 2.18 illustrates the application of h.r.c. fusegear in an industrial system. In applying fusegear a distinction is made between the requirement for protection against short-circuits due to electrical faults and overloads

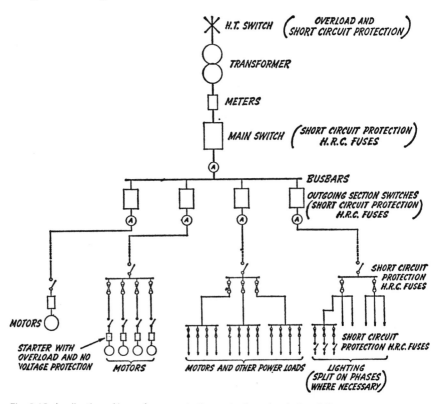

Fig. 2.18. Application of h.r.c. fusegear to the protection of an industrial installation

resulting from plant operating conditions. Short-circuit protection is required primarily at all positions in a system. Overload protection is required primarily at the control unit of the consuming equipment, as indicated in Fig. 2.18.

The h.r.c. fuses are essentially for short-circuit protection but also provide a measure of overload protection sufficient for busbar zones, distributor cables and other conductors. For overload protection of motors and other equipment, devices additional to the fuses are required. The fuses provide effective back-up fault protection for the contactors in control gear.

When fusegear is used on three-phase low-voltage systems with an earthed neutral, earth-fault protection depends entirely on the effectiveness of the earth return path to the star point of the transformer. The earth path impedance must be low enough to allow sufficient current to flow to blow the fuse quickly in the event of an earth fault.

Earth-leakage protection

For major low-voltage distribution circuits the separate protective scheme may be used, but for circuits and small installations the usual practice is to use an earth-leakage circuit-breaker (e.l.c.b.). Two main types are available, classed as fault-voltage and residual-current (r.c.c.b.) respectively.

The principle of the fault-voltage type is illustrated in Fig. 2.19. It will be seen that if current leaks from the element to the frame it flows back to the supply earth through the trip coil of the switch. Operation of the switch depends on the potential of the frame being high enough to produce a sufficient current flow through the impedance of the earth path. The effectiveness of the arrangement also depends on the frame being completely isolated from the body of the earth or any other protective conductors. If this is not the case, the parallel earth paths reduce the sensitivity of the trip so that it may fail to operate.

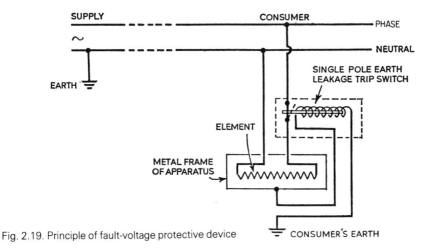

Fig. 2.19. Principle of fault-voltage protective device

The present tendency is to use current-operated e.l.c.b.s wherever there is any doubt that adequate protection will not be achieved by fuses or the voltage-operated e.l.c.b. However, the latter type can still be applied effectively in circumstances where the earth-loop impedance is very high and there is no risk of parallel paths. Reliable voltage-operated types are available as single-phase and three-phase units.

Fig. 2.20 shows the circuit of the fault-voltage operated circuit-breaker produced in one frame size for 60 A and 100 A ratings for use on single-phase 200–250 V installations. The breaker is designed to trip with a leakage current of about 25–40 mA and the tripping unit is protected from lightning by a discharge gap which is directly across the coil lead-outs. Earth electrode terminals E and frame terminals F are provided at both top and bottom of the breaker to facilitate wiring. The earth electrode is connected by an insulated cable to one of the two E terminals and all wires from the protected bonded metalwork are taken to either or both F terminals. In principle, the circuit is the same as that in Fig. 2.19.

It should be noted that to ensure correct functioning of this type of circuit-breaker, the resistance area of the earth electrode should be outside the resistance area of other metalwork (girders, water pipes, etc.) which make contact with the ground. An independent electrode is required which must be placed outside the resistance area of any parallel earth path.

An Ottermill three-phase residual current circuit-breaker is shown diagramatically in Figure 2.21. Fitted within its enclosure is a specially designed current sensor. All phase and neutral conductors are taken through the sensor within the unit, and under fault conditions the out-of-balance current is detected. The sensor then initiates tripping of the circuit-breaker via the shunt trip. The rated tripping currents depend upon the rating of the main breaker. The test switch simulates an earth fault and checks the integrity of the breaker mechanism and sensor unit circuitry. Ratings cover the range of 15–4000 A, 415 V.

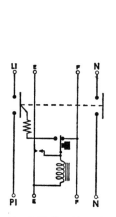

Fig. 2.20. Double-pole voltage protective device

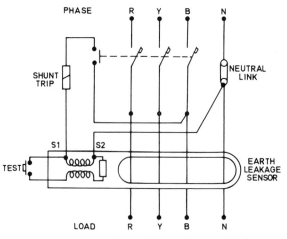

Fig. 2.21. Ottermill three-phase residual-current circuit-breaker

Earth-leakage protection of motors

In plants where persistent earth leakage is likely to be an abnormal fire risk, sensitive protection is applied to the motors to detect it at the incipient stage and disconnect the circuit without delay. To minimize the interruption to production, earth-leakage protection should be applied to individual motors (Fig. 2.22). However, where there is a large number of small motors individual protection is costly and the economical alternative is to apply the earth-leakage protection to one or more groups of motors. Although not as satisfactory as individual protection, such a scheme does offer a safeguard.

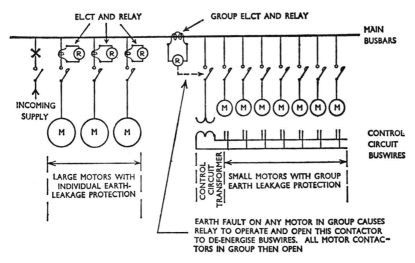

Fig. 2.22. Application of earth-leakage protection to individual large motors (left) and a group of small motors (right)

In planning a scheme, groups of motors are selected in relation to operational conditions. For example, a group that is sequenced or provides for several machine drives which must all run together, or not at all, is particularly suitable for group protection. Grouping may also be based on the total power of a number of motors; or motors above a certain power may be given individual protection while the smaller motors have group protection. The second type of scheme is also shown in Fig. 2.22.

Group protection involves the inclusion of the protective current transformers in the run of the busbars, and there must be some means whereby all the motors in the group are disconnected collectively in the event of an earth-leakage fault. Disconnection may be effected by a circuit-breaker supplying the group or by switching out a control circuit transformer which normally energizes all the hold-on coils of the line contactors of the group of motors. The arrangement of the control circuit transformer is shown in Figs. 2.22 and 2.23. The primary of the control circuit transformer is supplied from the main busbars through a contactor, and the hold-on coil of this contactor is in series with the normally closed

CONTROL CIRCUIT BUSWIRES TO CONTACTOR CIRCUITS

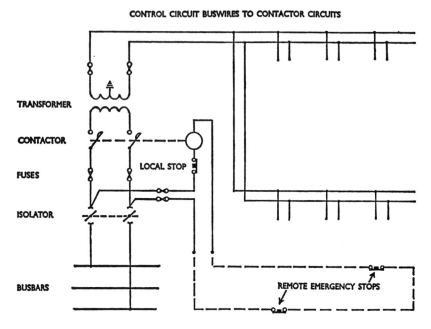

Fig. 2.23. Control circuit transformer with local and emergency pushbuttons for opening the main contactor

contacts of the earth-leakage relay. When this operates the contactor opens to disconnect the transformer from the main busbars and interrupt the supply to the control circuit buswires.

Whether for individual or group protection, the scheme involves the use of either a core-balance transformer with a single secondary winding, or a number of individual transformers each with its own secondary winding, the secondary windings being connected in star.

When it is vitally important that the earth-leakage protection must always be available, the control circuit must include a facility for testing. Fig. 2.24 shows a simple method of providing this facility on a core-balance scheme. It will be noted that there are two secondary windings on the transformer, and that winding SW is connected to a full-wave rectifier instead of being taken direct to an earth-leakage relay. The secondary current in SW resulting from an earth leakage is converted from a.c. to d.c. so that the relay is a telephone type, which is more sensitive than a standard a.c. relay.

The other secondary winding, TW, is connected across two primary lines through a switch which is closed to check the operation of the relay. As the switch momentarily short-circuits two supply lines, winding TW has a high resistance but it passes sufficient current to produce the flux required to induce in winding SW the current required to operate the relay. Special equipment is now available for testing earth-leakage circuit-breakers (residual current devices).

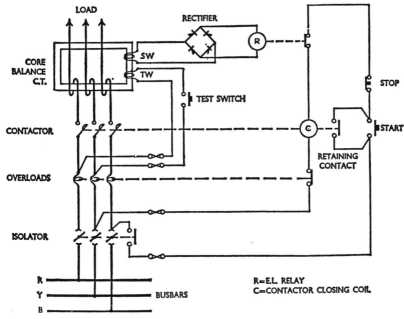

Fig. 2.24. Method of providing test facilities on earth-leakage protective gear

Earth-leakage protection of portable tools

Besides the possible use of BSI-approved double-insulated tools, which are permitted in factories without earthing of exposed metal, various protective schemes are available for reducing the risk of shock to operators of portable tools in industrial installations and temporary site installations. Under these conditions, floors tend to be more conductive and structural and other earthed metalwork more prevalent than elsewhere, and defects in earthings are therefore potentially more dangerous.

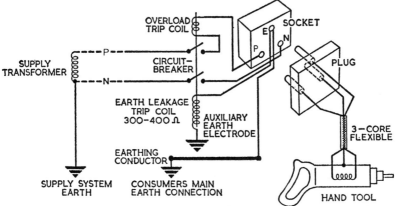

Fig. 2.25. Supplementary earth-leakage protection by fault-voltage protective device used for backing up overload protection, which is provided here by an excess-current circuit-breaker; this type of protection can be applied to an individual appliance or a group of portable tools

One method of protection is to use low-voltage tools and supply them through a step-down double-wound transformer at a reduced voltage, preferably 110 V or less. With the mid-point (single-phase) or star-point (three-phase) of a 110 V transformer secondary earthed, the maximum voltage to earth is reduced to 55 V single-phase or 64 V three-phase. A transformer tapping at 25 V is sometimes provided for supply to portable hand lamps.

Additional safety can be provided by earthing the mid-point or star-point of the transformer secondary through the trip coil of a fault-voltage circuit-breaker, although the use of an r.c.c.b. is preferable.

Monitoring earth connections of portable equipment

It is vitally important that the earth connection of portable tools and equipment should be maintained in particular locations, and a constant check can be kept on the circuit by the use of earth monitoring or proving units. A basic monitoring circuit is shown in Fig. 2.26. There are two

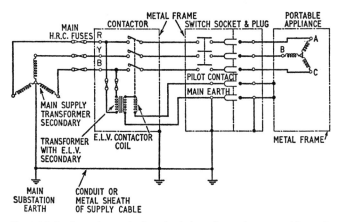

Fig. 2.26. Basic earth-monitoring circuit for a three-phase portable appliance. A light circulating current normally flows through the loop formed by the pilot and earth wires and energises the contactor hold-on coil. A break in the loop or a limitation of the current by a high-resistance joint will disconnect the supply

protective conductors which, when the main circuit is closed, provide a loop circuit for the continuously circulating current from the secondary of the e.l.v. transformer. This current also flows through the retaining coil holding the circuit switching unit closed. If either of the earth continuity conductors breaks or becomes detached, the retaining coil is de-energized and the main circuits open automatically.

Multi-outlet monitored-earth systems

The type of monitored-earth unit described above is designed for connection to a single appliance. The connection of a second tool to the unit would introduce a parallel earth path so that a circulating current through the monitored earth circuit would still be maintained if one of the earth loops became defective, and the supply would therefore not be cut off.

One multi-outlet monitored-earth system designed for small tools maintains a series earth path by employing special interlocked switches in the switched socket-outlets. With the socket-outlet supply switched off, the earth path is maintained through the closed contacts of an auxiliary switch in the outlet. The action of switching on the supply to the plug opens the auxiliary earth-switch contacts, thus introducing the pilot and earth leads of the flexible cable into the series monitored-earth circuit.

Insulation monitoring

The Findlay Durham and Brodie (FDB) line insulation monitor is produced to monitor single-phase or three-phase isolated power lines from 12 V to 550 V a.c., nominally at 50 Hz, and d.c. supplies from 24 V to 110 V. D.C. monitors need an auxiliary a.c. supply for energization via a transformer. A d.c. to a.c. converter would be required where an a.c. supply does not exist.

If an earth fault occurs on $\Phi1$ (Fig 2.27), then during the half-cycle that $\Phi2$ is positive with respect to $\Phi1$ a current will flow through the semiconductor D1, resistor R1, the constant-current source (CCS) and the R_{SENSE}. The CCS is nominally set to a limit of 12 mA. When the fault

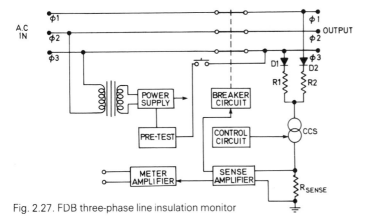

Fig. 2.27. FDB three-phase line insulation monitor

current exceeds a preset limit in the range 4 to 8 mA (user-adjustable) the breaker circuit is activated and the CCS is switched off. A delay of 1 ms is built in to prevent spurious tripping. This has the advantage that the proportion of the fault current that is greater than the preset level will only be present for 1 ms even though the breaker may take 20 ms to operate. In the event of the fault still being present the circuit will re-sample after approximately 100 ms.

The same procedure occurs for a fault on $\Phi2$ except that the opposite half-cycle is used and the current will flow through D2, R2. This method of alternate line monitoring at line frequency ensures that a balanced fault which could avoid detection cannot occur.

For three-phase supply the circuit is similar to that of the single-phase unit. This is possible because an earth fault on $\Phi 2$ will cause current to flow from $\Phi 1$ to $\Phi 3$ or both. This is of no consequence as the current is limited by the CCS. The difference will be that $\Phi 2$ will be monitored over a phase angle of 180°, as against 150° for a fault on $\Phi 1$ or $\Phi 3$. Each phase being considered will conduct to earth, ensuring that a balanced condition cannot occur.

Combined earth monitoring and earth-leakage protection

This FDB system has been designed to ensure that there is the continued presence of an earth connection at all times to portable or transportable electrical appliances. The unit conforms to BS 4444, 1969, i.e. it will automatically disconnect the supply when:

(a) its own power supply is lost or broken;
(b) the earth monitoring loop becomes broken (as by the failure of the protective conductor in a flexible cable);
(c) the protective monitoring loop (protective conductor and pilot) becomes short-circuited owing to, say, a heavy vehicle crushing the cable but still leaves the power intact to the remote apparatus; the change in conductor impedance to the remote apparatus will be detected and this will cause the supply to be disconnected; or
(d) the impedance of the earth loop varies: each unit is provided with a variable control to set the unit for any length of cable and its impedance. The unit will cause disconnection when the set impedance increases by 2 ohms. A test facility is incorporated which checks the open-circuit/high-impedance operation of the equipment. The input voltage is adjustable, 0–110/120 V, 220/250 V, 380/440 V and 550 V. The loop voltage is 7.5 V.

For single-phase and three-phase installations (Figs. 2.28 and 2.29) a further refinement permits a plug to be disconnected without tripping the earth monitoring system, i.e. the earth monitoring is only operative when the power is fed to the remote apparatus.

Three slave units can be powered from one master unit so that four separate circuits can be operated giving individual local control of earth monitoring.

Electrical hazardous areas

The flameproofing of equipment is necessary to guard against special industrial risks. Regulation 27 of the statutory Electricity (Factories) Special Regulations, 1908 and 1944, states:

'All conductors and apparatus exposed to the weather, wet, corrosion, *flammable surroundings or explosive atmosphere* (our italics), or used in any process for any purpose other than for lighting or power shall be so constructed, or protected, and such special precautions shall be taken as may be necessary adequately to prevent danger in view of such exposure or use.'

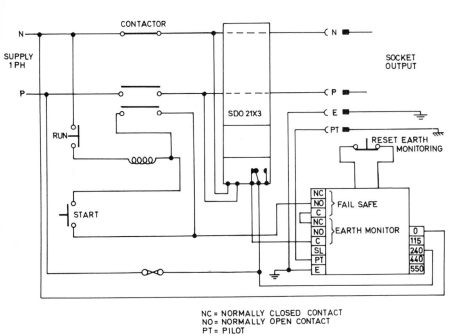

NC = NORMALLY CLOSED CONTACT
NO = NORMALLY OPEN CONTACT
PT = PILOT

Fig. 2.28. FDB single-phase earth monitoring and earth-leakage protection

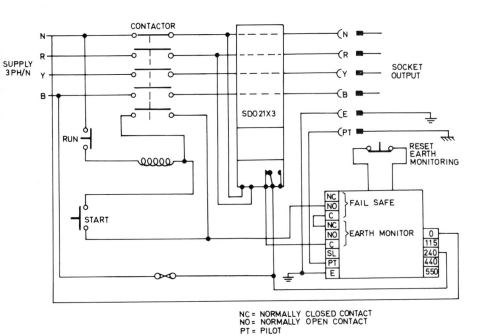

NC = NORMALLY CLOSED CONTACT
NO = NORMALLY OPEN CONTACT
PT = PILOT

Fig. 2.29. FDB three-phase earth monitoring and earth-leakage protection

Such hazards may arise in certain quarries, in coalmining, and in the chemical, paint and petroleum industries.

Certified flameproof electrical apparatus and fittings will prevent the transmission of flame such as will ignite flammable gases. They formerly bore an emblem in the form of a crown outline containing the letters FLP. Due to the complexity of the potentially dangerous situations, this simple (at one time all-embracing) emblem has been superseded by lettering which is more informative.

Hazardous areas are categorized into zones. Zone 0 is an area or enclosed space where the flammable material is always present. Zone 1 is an area where the flammable material is processed, handled and stored and where there is a flammable atmosphere during normal operations. Zone 2 is an area where the flammable material, although processed or stored, is controlled so that a flammable atmosphere is only likely to occur under abnormal conditions.

In the United Kingdom, equipment must comply with the requirements of the British Approvals Service for Electrical Equipment in Flammable Atmospheres (BASEEFA). FLP is now replaced by Ex (Fig. 2.30(a)). European Economic Community (ECC) countries place Ex inside a hexagon (b).

Additions to the required type of protection are:

Ex d   flameproof enclosure
Ex e   increased safety
Ex ia   increased safety (higher category)
Ex ib   increased safety (lower category)
Ex o   oil immersion
Ex p   pressurized
Ex q   sand or quartz filler
Ex s   special protection
Ex n   other type of protection

Pressurization as a form of protection against the entry of explosive gases is achieved by introducing air, CO_2, or an inert gas, under a slight pressure to the interior of fittings.

Where more than one type of protection is necessary, the symbol must appear outside the crown, with the main protection concept given first. Fig. 2.30(c) illustrates oil and pressurization.

Explosive gases are also classified under group numbers: Group I is gas encountered in coal-mining such as methane (firedamp); Group II includes various gases met in industry, such as cellulose vapour, petrol, benzine, amyl acetate, etc.; Group III is coal and coke gas and ethylene oxide; Group IV covers excluded gases, i.e. where there is no flameproof general approval

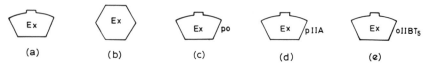

(a)   (b)   (c)   (d)   (e)

Fig. 2.30. Equipment symbols for hazardous areas (see text)

such as acetylene, carbon disulphide and hydrogen, although approval may be given in individual cases. The full list is given in BS 229.

Group II can be sub-divided into IIA (propane), IIB (ethylene) and IIC (hydrogen). As an example of this classification, Fig. 2.30(d) stands for pressurized Group II gas.

Temperature indications are shown in IEC Publication 79, Electrical Apparatus for Explosive Gas Atmospheres, as follows:

Classification	Maximum surface temperature
T_1	450°C
T_2	300°C
T_3	200°C
T_4	135°C
T_5	100°C
T_6	85°C

Fig. 2.30(e) may be read as 'oil immersed, group IIB with a maximum surface temperature of 100°C.'

Protection of hazardous areas by electronic equipment

For low-power requirements *intrinsically safe* methods may be employed and are suitable for all gas groups and zones. The term 'intrinsically safe' is applied to apparatus in which electric sparking in gases is incapable of causing an explosion.

The zener safety barrier circuit (Fig. 2.31) is designed to limit the energy which can be transferred from the safe area to the hazardous area even under fault conditions. The zener safety barrier incorporates a resistor of a

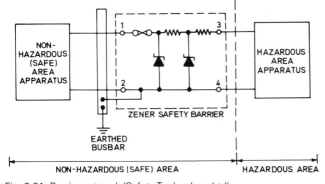

Fig. 2.31. Barrier network (Safety Technology Ltd)

value such that the output is short-circuit proof. The fuse protection will only become operative either in the event of incorrect polarity connection in the safe area, or if an excessive voltage is applied to terminals 1 and 2.

At least two zener diodes are used so that the zener barrier assembly remains safe under component failure conditions. The fuse is incorporated so that it is possible to determine a maximum design power for the zener diodes. The base line terminals 2 and 4 must be securely bonded to earth.

3 Special-purpose supplies

The standard electricity supplies are not suitable for all purposes and special equipment is needed to provide supplies at a.c. and d.c. voltages required to meet specific requirements.

Supplies at a.c. voltages lower than standard values, required to ensure the safe use of portable tools and lighting, can be provided by step-down double-wound transformers with the centre of the secondary connected to earth. Fig. 3.1 shows a typical arrangement to provide a 110 V a.c. supply for portable tools, and including a further safeguard by earthing through an r.c.c.b.

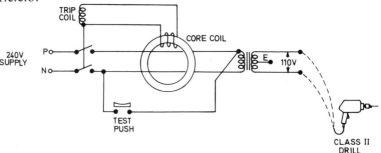

Fig. 3.1. Double-wound transformer providing 110 V a.c. supply for portable tools with a voltage to earth of 55 V (a residual-current earth-leakage circuit-breaker is an added protection)

Portable lighting used inside boilers, tanks and other locations where there is a risk of personnel receiving a shock from a 110 V supply should be supplied at 12 V through a step-down transformer unit. The transformer secondary must be connected to earth at the centre point so that the maximum voltage to earth does not exceed 6 V.

On large building sites special load centres may be used to provide a supply to socket-outlets for 110 V and 240 V single-phase and 415 V three-phase circuits. A typical arrangement is shown in Fig. 3.2. All socket-outlets are required to be protected by earth-leakage circuit-breakers, preferably of the residual-current type.

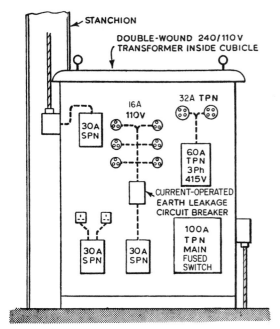

STANCHION

DOUBLE-WOUND 240/110V
TRANSFORMER INSIDE CUBICLE

16A
110V

32A TPN

30A
SPN

60A
TPN
3Ph
415V

CURRENT-OPERATED
EARTH LEAKAGE
CIRCUIT BREAKER

100A
TPN
MAIN
FUSED
SWITCH

30A
SPN

30A
SPN

Fig. 3.2. Load centre for temporary installation

Voltage-regulated a.c. supplies

For some industrial purposes there is a requirement for an a.c. supply at a precisely regulated voltage, which must be met by using an appropriate voltage regulator. Various types of regulator are available. Fig. 3.3 shows schematically a type developed by Foster Transformers Ltd. and incorporating a motor-operated regulating transformer which supplies the primary of a buck and boost transformer.

The regulator transformer T1 is connected between phase and neutral while transformer T2 has its secondary winding connected between the input and output line terminals. The primary winding of T2 is supplied from T1, one end being connected to a fixed tapping on T1 and the other end being connected to the moving brush. When the brush is opposite the tap no voltage is induced in T2; thus the output voltage will be equal to the input voltage at the terminals P1–N. As the brush moves up the winding, the voltage across the primary and therefore across the secondary of T2 will increase progressively. The polarity is such that the secondary voltage is added to the supply voltage applied to P1–N so that there is a rise in the output voltage across P2–N. Conversely, if the brush of T1 moves downwards from the fixed tapping, the voltage on T2 will rise but the polarity will be reversed, thus reducing the output voltage across P2–N.

It follows that changes in supply voltage can be corrected by movement of the brush of T1 to maintain the output voltage constant, provided that the changes in supply voltage are no greater than the maximum voltage that can be developed across the secondary of T2. If the tapping on T1 is placed in the centre of the winding, then equal plus and minus mains voltage variations can be corrected, giving equal buck and boost. If the tap is offset then the buck and boost voltages will be unequal, e.g. for an input range of +5 per cent and −15 per cent, the tap would be 25 per cent up the winding.

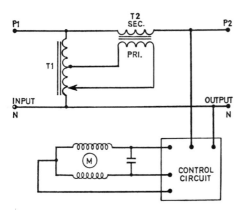

Fig. 3.3. Connections of automatic voltage regulator

These Foster voltage stabilizers are available for single-phase and three-phase service, equipment for the latter being supplied either with individual phase control or simultaneous phase control. For the former, three single-phase regulators are connected in a star bank, and each line-neutral voltage is monitored and stabilized separately, thus providing for conditions where load currents and/or input voltages are unbalanced.

D.C. supplies from rectifiers

Special-purpose d.c. supplies are still used extensively in many industrial plants. In some cases the supply is required to power the d.c. motors which are essential for certain variable-speed drives. At one time, when a public d.c. supply was no longer available for motors, this was obtained from works substations and feeders to individual motors or to a general distribution system. The early substations were equipped with some form of rotating convertor but later mercury-arc rectifiers were used. With further development of these and other forms of static rectifier, where practicable the rectifier was designed and constructed as an integral part of the motor control equipment so that d.c. distribution was eliminated, the standard a.c. supply being taken direct to the control unit (see Chapter 8).

Sources of d.c. supply are also required for various industrial purposes, particularly electrochemical processes for producing metals, gases and chemical compounds; electroplating work; and battery forming and charging. For some processes, the d.c. power requirement is substantial. In the production of aluminium, for example, the requirement is for from 40 000–100 000 A or more at from 500–1000 V.

Semiconductor rectifier equipments

Requirements for d.c. supplies are today met largely by the use of solid-state rectifier equipments, consisting of different arrangements of diodes. These semiconductor diodes conduct easily in one direction but block the current flow in the opposite direction. In circuit diagrams the schematic symbol for a diode is as shown at Y and Z in Fig. 3.4. Assuming the current flows from positive to negative, the arrowhead of the symbol indicates the direction in which the diode conducts easily. The terminal represented by the arrowhead is the anode and that represented by the line is the cathode.

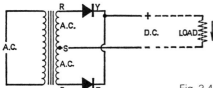

Fig. 3.4. Full-wave rectifier by solid-state diode circuit

The normal flow through a diode is termed forward current and it is maintained by the forward voltage. The voltage acting in the opposite direction, i.e. that in which there is normally no appreciable current flow, is termed the reverse voltage. If this voltage exceeds a particular value it will cause a reverse current to leak through the diode from the cathode to the anode.

Diodes are designed to pass a forward current of a specified maximum value, and to withstand a reverse voltage of a specified maximum value. If these values are exceeded, a diode becomes useless. For circuits carrying a current exceeding the rating of a single diode, two or more are connected in parallel. If the applied voltage is greater that the rated reverse voltage of a single diode, two or more diodes are connected in series. Series-parallel connections are also used (Fig. 3.5).

To rectify alternating current, diodes are used either singly or in groups, depending on the forward current they have to pass and the reverse voltage they have to withstand. Fig. 3.4 shows a simple arrangement of two diodes connected for full-wave rectification. Diode Y conducts during every alternate half-cycle of the a.c. wave, and diode Z conducts during every other alternate half-cycle. When R is positive with respect to S and T, current flows from R through diode Y and through the load to S. When the diode Y is conducting, the diode Z blocks the circuit from Y and thus prevents the secondary winding of the transformer being short-circuited. When diode Z is conducting, T is positive with respect to S and R, and diode Y blocks the circuit from Z. Whichever diode is conducting, current always flows through the load in the same direction.

Fig. 3.5 shows a multiple series-parallel bridge connection of diodes for full-wave rectification, which functions in the same way as the arrangement in Fig. 3.4.

Present-day rectifier equipment incorporates either germanium or silicon diodes. Some years ago the germanium diode had certain

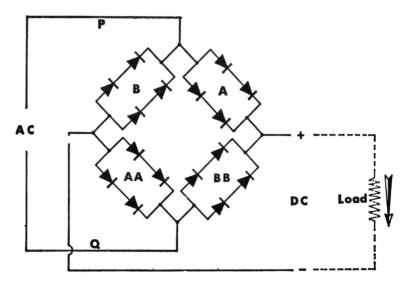

Fig. 3.5. Arrangement of diodes for full-wave rectification

advantages over the silicon diode but further development of the latter made it superior for all applications except for producing the lowest d.c. voltages. Germanium diodes give a higher efficiency when they can be used without series or bridge connection, which is the case, for example, below about 50 V d.c. However, even at low voltages it is better to use silicon diodes if the ambient temperature is higher than 40°C. At higher voltages, silicon diodes are preferred because they withstand higher reverse voltages, and produced with dual polarity the diodes allow for simple arrangements to be achieved for operation up to 1000 V d.c. with two diodes in series, one connected to the a.c. busbar and the other to the d.c. busbar (Fig. 3.6).

Large semiconductor rectifiers comprise a number of individual diodes or series strings of diodes which are connected in parallel. For the majority of industrial and electronic applications there may be as many as 50 strings connected in parallel. Fig. 3.6 shows a typical connection diagram for a small equipment.

It will be noted that the incoming three-phase supply is connected to the primary of a transformer which is usually needed to change the voltage of the supply to a value which, applied to the rectifier bank, will result in the required d.c. output voltage. Relatively small capacity single-phase half-way rectifiers can be connected directly to the a.c. supply but this is seldom feasible because of the difficulty of obtaining the d.c. voltage required. The same applies to larger capacity single-phase and three-phase double-way or bridge rectifiers. It is not permissible to connect a three-phase half-wave rectifier to the mains because of returning direct current to the neutral. Consequently such rectifiers must be supplied by a main transformer with a separate neutral.

In addition to providing the essential a.c. voltage transformation, a transformer is also used to increase the number of phases, e.g. the three-phase supply can be changed to a six-phase supply for application to the rectifier bank. Increasing the number of phases of the supply to the rectifier bank also increases the pulse number, i.e. the number of d.c. output pulses per a.c. cycle, and therefore minimizes the disturbances to the a.c. supply system due to harmonics in the input to the rectifier unit.

Special consideration is given to the protection of the semiconductor diodes. Overcurrent protection is achieved by relays tripping the main a.c. circuit-breaker, the current being measured by either a.c. or d.c. current transformers. A combination of both instantaneous and thermal relay elements protects against most overcurrents.

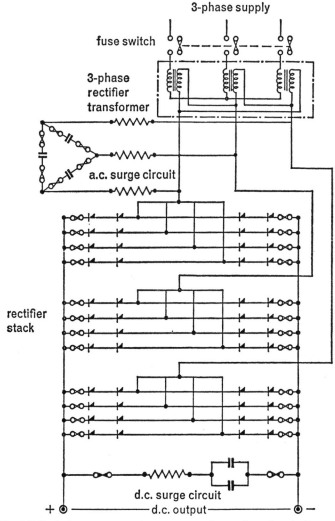

Fig. 3.6. Typical arrangement of components of a small semiconductor rectifier equipment

The rectifier is also protected against over-voltages which can be produced by the diodes themselves, due to the sudden cessation of the reverse current which flows for a short time after forward conduction, or by switching operations, lightning and faults on the supply side of the rectifier transformer. Over-voltages may also appear from the load side due to switching of inductive circuits or machines regenerating. As shown in Fig. 3.6, there are both a.c. and d.c. surge circuits to protect against over-voltages.

Protection against the effects of a diode failure is provided by the fuses shown in Fig. 3.6. This protection is essential because if a string of diodes fails in service there is a short-circuit across the transformer winding and reverse current is fed into the fault by the other phases. The rate of rise of reverse current is very high so the fuse is designed to cut off the fault current at a small fraction of its prospective value.

Rectifier transformer connections

Various transformer connections are used to meet different requirements. For example, the d.c. voltage obtainable from a six-phase half-wave circuit without series diodes (Fig. 3.8) is only about a half that from a bridge circuit (Fig. 3.7), but as the direct current passes through only one rectifier arm at a time instead of two arms in series, the forward voltage drop and losses are halved. With the higher voltage silicon diodes now available, the six-phase half-wave circuit can be used for up to about 300 V d.c.

The double-star connection (Fig. 3.8) is used because, with the two star groups operating in parallel, each rectifier arm carries current for 120° (one third of a cycle) whereas with the alternative six-phase modes of operation, each arm carries current for only 60°. The connection therefore ensures maximum utilization of the transformer windings. Double-star operation is obtained conventionally by connecting the two star points of the secondary winding through a voltage sharing transformer (interphase transformer). A simpler and more economical method is to have a star-connected primary winding and thus eliminate the interphase unit (Fig. 3.9). With this connection, the current-carrying period increases sharply from 60° at minimum load and at about 25 per cent load becomes 120°, as with the double-star connection.

Although the connection shown in Fig. 3.9 gives maximum efficiency and is especially suitable for heavy currents, it has the disadvantage of giving a voltage rise below 25 per cent load. If this is not acceptable, or if the primary winding cannot be star-connected, the interphase transformer arrangement must be used. It should also be noted that the six-phase connections are not used if diodes have to be connected in series to obtain high d.c. voltages. The same result is achieved more simply, efficiently and economically with the bridge connection shown in Fig. 3.7 which also gives six-pulse rectification, as with the six-phase connections.

The six-pulse rectifier equipments draw a current from the supply containing undesirable fifth and seventh harmonics which produce distortion of the supply voltage particularly if the local supply system is of limited capacity or high impedance. It is therefore necessary to limit six-pulse rectifier loading according to the capacity of the supply system.

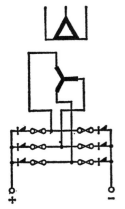

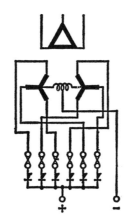

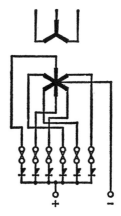

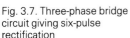

Fig. 3.7. Three-phase bridge circuit giving six-pulse rectification

Fig. 3.8. Six-phase half-wave circuit with interphase transformer

Fig. 3.9. Six-phase half-wave circuit without interphase transformer

In Britain, the general recommendation is a maximum of approximately 0.5 MW per 100 MVA of supply short-circuit capacity. For rectifier loads higher than this 12-pulse operation is desirable so that the fifth and seventh harmonics are eliminated. Although the eleventh and thirteenth harmonics are then present, their effect is smaller, consequently it is permitted to increase the rectifier loading to about 2 MW per 100 MVA of supply short-circuit capacity. This figure is increased to 4 MW for 24-pulse rectification and higher for 36-pulse rectification when the waveform is then practically sinusoidal.

Connections for 12-pulse rectification are shown in Fig. 3.10. The secondary windings are in two six-phase groups which are given a phase displacement by interstar connections or overwinds. Such windings are sometimes referred to as zigzag or dog-leg windings. Interphase transformers are used as necessary to obtain 120° of current carrying in each rectifier arm.

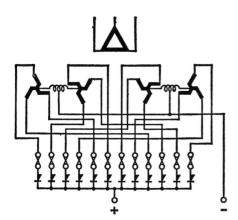

Fig. 3.10. 12-phase half-wave circuit using one transformer with phase displacement by interstar secondary windings

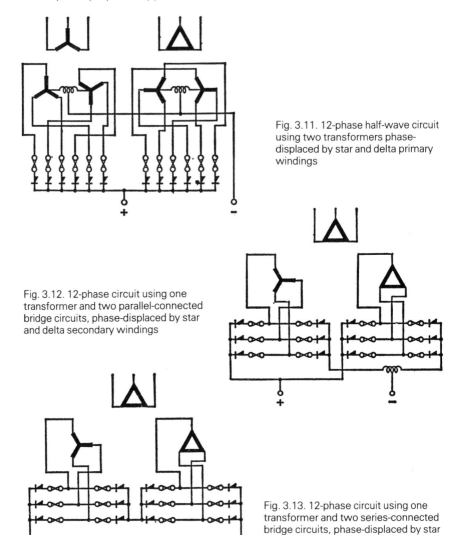

Fig. 3.11. 12-phase half-wave circuit using two transformers phase-displaced by star and delta primary windings

Fig. 3.12. 12-phase circuit using one transformer and two parallel-connected bridge circuits, phase-displaced by star and delta secondary windings

Fig. 3.13. 12-phase circuit using one transformer and two series-connected bridge circuits, phase-displaced by star and delta secondary windings

When two or more separate d.c. circuits are required, the effect of 12-pulse loading can be achieved by winding one transformer with a star primary and the other with a delta primary (Fig. 3.11).

When the voltage is too high to be able to use a half-wave type of circuit without having diodes in series, it is advantageous to use bridge circuits. Fig. 3.12 shows how 12-pulse rectification can be obtained by using star and delta secondary winding supplying two three-phase bridge circuits connected in parallel. For higher d.c. voltages series connection can be employed as shown in Fig. 3.13. This also gives 12-pulse rectification but without an interphase transformer.

Rectifier d.c. output voltage control

Control of the d.c. voltage of semiconductor rectifier units can be effected by varying the output voltage of the transformer secondary winding using on-load or off-load tap-changers. The d.c. voltage is adjusted in steps which may be acceptable for certain applications such as battery charging for which off-load tap-changing is also suitable. For process control the requirement may be for on-load voltage adjustment in small increments. If the increment is fairly small then on-load tap-changing involves too many tappings from the transformer and some other form of voltage regulation is necessary.

Infinitely variable regulation is obtained with a sliding or rolling contact variable-ratio regulating transformer which may be connected before or after the main transformer. Transductors (saturable reactors) can also be used to give stepless control. The most advanced and rapid method of d.c. voltage control is to use a scheme based on thyristors incorporated in the semiconductor rectifier.

As represented in Fig. 3.14, a simple transductor consists of two cores with an a.c. and d.c. winding on each. The d.c. windings are connected in series opposition while the a.c. windings may be connected either in series or in parallel. The a.c. circuit is connected to the supply and the d.c.

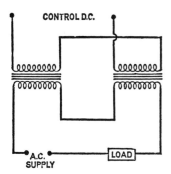

Fig. 3.14. Arrangement of simple transductor windings

control circuit is connected to a source of variable d.c. voltage which enables the direct current to be varied. In this way the saturation of the core material can be varied to regulate the impedance of the a.c. winding and therefore the current in the load circuit.

With no direct current in the control winding the impedance of the load circuit is high and the current is a minimum but if an increasing direct current is supplied to the control winding, the impedance diminishes and the current increases.

Although the transductor is a current regulating rather than a voltage regulating device, the effect is the same as when the voltage applied to a circuit is regulated to control the current. Transductors are used to control the current supplied to equipments such as electric furnaces, motors and special lighting installations.

Transformer-rectifier unit for heavy currents

Referred to as saturable reactors, transductors are used in the voltage regulating scheme of the heavy current Rectiformer shown in Fig. 3.15. A development of GEC Rectifiers Ltd., the Rectiformer is a factory-built unit combining the transformer and rectifier as a single equipment which is compact and can be installed indoors or outdoors on one foundation. Intended for applications requiring above 25 000 A, the rectifier sub-unit can be adapted to suit either bridge or single-way connections. The latter is used whenever possible because it allows a simple rectifier layout arrangement.

For the sake of clarity Fig. 3.15 shows only a few of the silicon diodes and diode fuses. A combination of a regulating transformer and saturable reactors is used to control the d.c. output since with heavy current electro-chemical loads it is often necessary to vary the voltage by 50 per cent. The regulating transformer is equipped with an on-load tap-changer

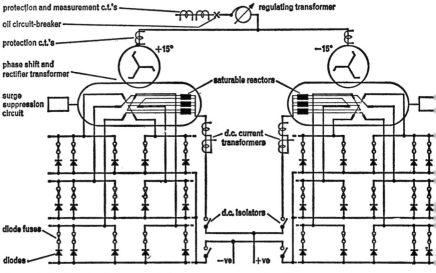

Fig. 3.15. Typical circuit diagram of single-way connected Rectiformer

for coarse voltage steps and the saturable reactors provide for smooth fine voltage trimming. This combination provides the infinitely variable voltage regulation needed for accurate and continuous control.

The tap-changer and the saturable reactors can be operated independently on manual control but normally are under automatic control. A simplified diagram of the automatic control scheme is shown in Fig. 3.16. The error signal between the load current and the reference setting is amplified and fed into the control winding of the saturable reactor which acts to adjust the load current to the value corresponding to the reference setting. When the saturable reactor range is not sufficient to provide the necessary adjustment to reduce the error signal, the limiter calls for a higher or lower tap position as required.

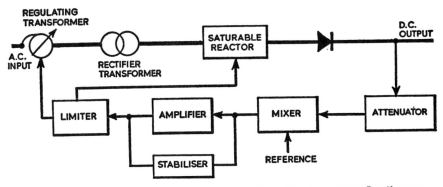

Fig. 3.16. Block diagram of the automatic control circuit used in heavy-current Rectiformers

Thyristor control schemes

An advanced and rapid method of controlling the d.c. output voltage of a semiconductor rectifier equipment is to use a scheme based on thyristors incorporated in the diode assembly. Where applicable, such a scheme provides for an integrated all solid-state control system with an almost instantaneous response to weak control signals.

Originally termed a 'silicon controlled rectifier', the thyristor may be considered as a switched diode, i.e. it combines the rectifying properties of a diode with those of a switch. The schematic symbol for a thyristor is shown in Fig. 3.17. Like the diode it has an anode and a cathode, and a third electrode which is termed a gate. A thyristor blocks reverse current and its special feature is that it also blocks forward current until it is turned-on (i.e. switched on) by a gating pulse; this is a short pulse of low-voltage current applied between the gate and the cathode.

Fig. 3.17. Principle of thyristor operation

If a constant forward voltage is applied to a thyristor which is then turned-on, it continues to pass forward current indefinitely either until the forward voltage is removed or until a reverse voltage, greater than the forward voltage, is superimposed on the forward voltage. The gate cannot be used to turn-off the thyristor. However, it is only necessary to remove the forward voltage, or apply the reverse voltage for a few microseconds, to turn off the thyristor.

As shown in Fig. 3.18, when an a.c. voltage is applied and the thyristor is turned-on at instant X (when the thyristor is forward-biased) the thyristor conducts until the forward voltage falls to zero at instant Y. It cannot conduct again unless a further gating pulse is applied at instant Z. Between instants Y and Z, the thyristor is reverse-biased and therefore blocks the circuit against reverse current.

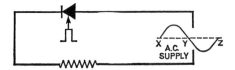

Fig. 3.18. Operation of thyristor on a.c. supply

To cause a thyristor to conduct every alternate half-cycle, like an ordinary diode, a timed series of gating pulses is applied. Unlike a diode, however, a thyristor can be turned-on at any desired instant during each forward-biasing half-cycle, and with this form of control, the thyristor can be made to conduct for only parts of half-cycles. The shorter the time during which the thyristor conducts in each half-cycle, the less is the average voltage during the half-cycle. Thus, by varying the instant at which the thyristor is turned on, the output voltage can be varied.

Fig. 3.19 shows the arrangement of two thyristors for obtaining a variable-voltage d.c. output. The circuits for producing the regulated series of gating pulses are not shown. Applied to the thyristors, these pulses cause one thyristor to conduct while the other blocks.

A typical control application of thyristors is shown in basic form in Fig. 3.20. The purpose of the circuit is to permit a d.c. supply to be switched rapidly and repeatedly on and off across a load (e.g. a motor), thus causing the average current through the load to vary according to the rate of on/off switching. When Thy. 1 is turned on by a gating pulse, capacitor C becomes charged in the direction indicated by the 'solid' polarity symbols above it, i.e. it becomes charged in the direction of polarity of the supply. The charging current of C flows via the circuit P–T–V. When the charging current ceases to flow into C, i.e. it is fully charged, forward voltage no longer exists across Thy. 1, which therefore is turned off.

When Thy. 2 is turned on by a gating pulse it allows current to flow through the load. With Thy. 2 conducting, C discharges through it via diode D and inductance L, i.e. via the circuit P–Q–R–S–T. Due to the inductance of L, C not only discharges but also becomes charged in the reverse direction, as indicated by the dotted polarity symbols below it.

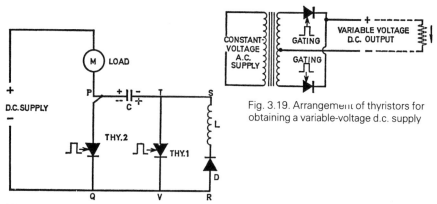

Fig. 3.19. Arrangement of thyristors for obtaining a variable-voltage d.c. supply

Fig. 3.20. A typical control application of thyristors

Diode D holds this reverse charge on the capacitor, since it is blocking the flow. When Thy. 1 is turned on a second time, it applies the reversed voltage of C across Thy. 2, which is therefore turned off, thus preventing further current flow through the load. The cycle of operations may then be repeated.

Thyristors are used in various power units to provide variable voltage d.c. supplies for motors and other equipment. They are also used in static inverter units to provide an a.c. supply from a d.c. source, which may be a battery forming part of an equipment to provide a standby supply for a.c. circuits normally connected to the mains.

Battery charging

For many purposes a d.c. supply from a battery is essential and so provision must be made for charging. With d.c. mains available simple arrangements of resistors, switches and instruments may suffice, but as usually only an a.c. supply is available, some form of rectifier unit is necessary. Most battery chargers are now static units incorporating semiconductor diodes.

Fig. 3.21 shows the components and circuits of a scheme based on a static rectifier. The output voltage can be adjusted within limits by tappings on the transformer secondary and the charging current by the rheostat in series with the ammeter. As an alternative to this ammeter, Fig. 3.21 shows

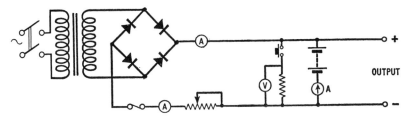

Fig. 3.21. Battery-charging equipment

a centre-zero ammeter in the battery connection which serves to indicate both charge or discharge currents. The diagram also shows two circuits for checking the state of the battery, either of which may be used. With one circuit, operation of the pushbutton puts a discharge resistor across the battery to simulate the load condition and the state of charge of the battery is shown by the hydrometer and voltmeter reading. The second circuit has an ammeter in series with the discharge resistor.

Transistor charger

The a.c. supply input to the chloride standby charger (Fig. 3.22) is applied to a double-wound transformer, the secondary of which is rectified via MR1. The resultant d.c. is smoothed by C4 and fed to the collectors TR7 and TR8. These two regulator transistors are paralleled by having their emitters connected together via R8 and R7, which act as current-sharing

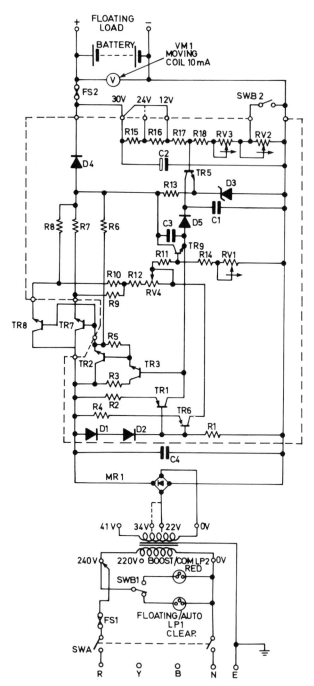

Fig. 3.22. Chloride transistor charger. Variable resistors have the following effect: RV1 controls current limit, RV2 sets float/auto voltage, RV3 sets boost/comm. voltage, RV4 sets short-circuit current limit

resistors to ensure equal power dissipation for each transistor. Current then passes through D4 to charge the battery. D4 prevents the battery discharging through the charger circuit when the charger is on. A potential divider circuit is formed by R15, R16, R17 (depending on the number of cells) R18, RV3 and RV2. RV3 gives an adjustment setting for commission (boost) voltage and RV2 gives an adjustment setting for auto (float) voltage setting such that a percentage of the battery voltage is applied to the base of TR5 and compared with the reference voltage zener diode D3 fed via R13 from the charger output voltage. The collector of TR5 is fed from a constant current source formed by TR1 and R2 with a reference voltage produced by the diodes D1 and D2 which are fed via R1.

The base of TR3 is fed from the collector of TR1 and the base current is diverted by the conduction of TR5 via D5 which protects TR5 against reverse transient voltages. Hence, as the battery voltage increases, the conduction of TR5 increases and the base current of TR3 is reduced. This in turn reduces the drive to TR2 via R3 and the emittter of TR3. The reduction in base current of TR2 reduces the drive to the regulator TR7 and TR8 and hence the charging current, produced across the resistors R7 and R8, is added to a voltage across R12 and RV4 produced by a constant current from TR6. The voltage from the current flowing in R11, R14 and RV1 is added to the above sum and applied to the base of TR4. TR4 when conducting reduces the drive current to the base of TR3; hence the charging current RV1 controls the charge current limit and RV4 controls the short-circuit current limit.

Constant-voltage charging

Fig. 3.23 shows a scheme to give a constant output voltage irrespective of both mains voltage and load variations. In principle, the circuit changes progressively from a single-phase to a three-phase rectifier bridge circuit as the load current increases from zero to its full value. The two transformers T1 and T2 have their primaries connected in series, T2 is shunted by a

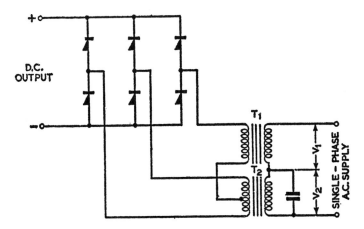

Fig. 3.23. Constant-voltage charging equipment

capacitor, and the secondaries are Scott-connected. By suitable design it can be so arranged that at full load the voltages across the primaries V1 and V2 are displaced by 90°. In effect, the single-phase supply is converted to two-phase and then to three-phase and applied to the diodes.

As the load current falls V1 decreases and the voltages V1 and V2 swing towards each other so that the displacement is no longer 90° and, in effect, one phase of the three phases is lost progressively. The system reverts to single-phase from T2 only at no load.

The scheme also provides a high degree of mains voltage-variation compensation as the voltages V1 and V2 must always sum vectorially to the value of the mains voltage. A change in the latter produces a change in magnitude and phase displacement between V1 and V2 and as these two effects tend to neutralize one another, the d.c. output voltage remains reasonably constant.

Emergency power supply schemes

At one time installed to meet lighting regulations in cinemas and theatres, emergency battery schemes are now used widely in many types of buildings not only to provide lighting but also to maintain essential supplies for fire alarm systems, electromagnetic chucks and process control and other services.

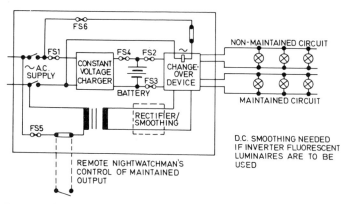

Fig. 3.24. Chloride maintained system

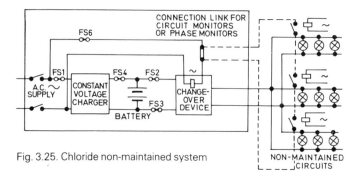

Fig. 3.25. Chloride non-maintained system

Emergency lighting

In the *maintained* system of chloride standby (Fig. 3.24), output to the luminaires is maintained at all times. The options of non-maintained or controllable maintained output are provided as standard. When the non-maintained outputs or controlled maintained outputs are used circuit monitors may be provided.

With *non-maintained* units (Fig. 3.25) the standby lamps are only illuminated when the a.c. supply fails. The d.c. output is connected automatically to the luminaires when the a.c. supply to the coil of the changeover device is interrupted by supply failure, phase failure or remote circuit monitors.

Electroplating d.c. supplies

The low voltage d.c. supply required for electroplating and similar processes can be obtained from generators but these are being superseded by transformer–rectifier units.

The voltage required varies from less than 1 V for silver plating to over 7 V for hard chrome deposition; and for barrel plating from 6 to 16 V is necessary, depending on the type of barrel and the solution employed. Anodic oxidation of aluminium by the sulphuric acid process requires about 15 V, or up to 24 V for the treatment of 'architectural' sections, and up to 60 V may be needed for the chromic acid process. Even higher voltages are used for hard anodizing and other specialized applications.

Transformer–rectifier units are available with various output voltages to meet the requirements for specific processes. The transformer reduces the mains voltage to a value some 25 per cent above that of the rated full-load output of the equipment, e.g. about 10 V for an 8 V unit, and the low a.c. voltage is rectified.

The most economical usage of the a.c. mains supply is obtained with three-phase rectifiers, the unit being arranged to give phase-multiplication to provide hexaphase (six-phase) at a ripple content of better than 5 per cent. Single-phase rectifiers are available for small outputs up to 150 A but a comparatively high a.c. ripple content makes them unsuitable for chromium plating. The latest types of rectifier use silicon diodes.

The output voltage of a transformer-rectifier unit is regulated by adjustment of the input voltage to the transformer primary, using an auto-transformer with multiple tappings or a stepless regulator. The latter is preferred when frequent voltage changes are necessary, and if the regulator is motor-driven it can be controlled automatically to provide constant current or voltage.

Fig. 3.26 shows the circuits of a Canning silicon transformer–rectifier unit with a motorized stepless voltage regulator. This is operated by pushbuttons on the meter panel and there is a handwheel for emergency manual operation. The panel also has pushbuttons for the remote control of the a.c. contactor. The contacts of the silicon rectifier overload protection are connected in series with the contactor trip coil.

Generators for electroplating are either shunt-wound or separately excited types. The latter provides for more precise control and avoids the risk of accidental reversal of generator polarity. Double-commutator type generators are used with the connections so arranged that two voltages, one double the other, are obtained at the same time. The scheme is convenient for plating shops where both still and barrel-plating units are operated from one generator. As shown in Fig. 3.27, the scheme is essentially a three-wire system with the plating barrels connected to the

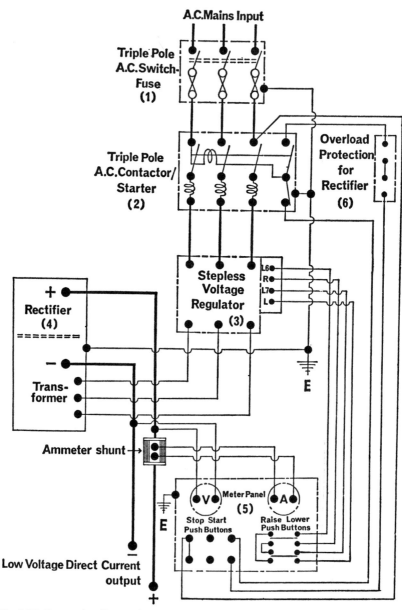

Fig. 3.26. Connection diagram for electroplating transformer–rectifier unit

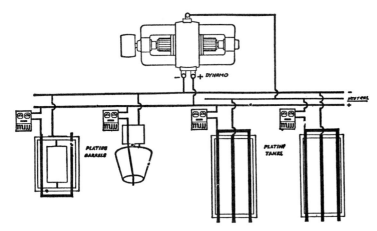

Fig. 3.27. Double-commutator generator supplying three-wire d.c. electroplating supply

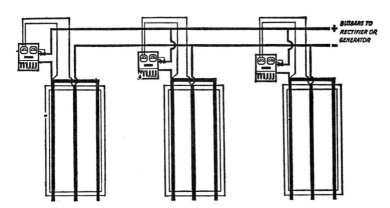

Fig. 3.28. System for control of supply to several plating tanks

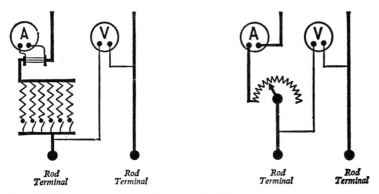

Fig. 3.29. Two common types of resistance board

two outer busbars and the still plating vats connected between the central neutral busbar and either of the outer busbars. The load must be balanced so that normally an equal current is taken from each commutator.

Where a number of plating units receive a supply from a single d.c. source, any adjustment of the output voltage would affect all the units. For individual control of the voltage and current to each unit, the usual practice is to maintain the voltage on the busbars at a relatively constant value and provide a variable resistance board for each unit (Fig. 3.28). The two common types of resistance board are shown in Fig. 3.29. The series type is for up to 50 A and the parallel type for higher currents.

4 Lighting circuits

In considering the wiring circuits for lighting installations it must be emphasized that to meet a requirement in the 15th Edition of the IEE Regulations for Electrical Installations, every circuit must have a circuit protective conductor connected to a consumer's earth terminal adjacent to the consumer's terminals. This provision therefore applies to all lighting circuits at normal voltages, and to provide for connection of the lighting points and switch boxes to the circuit protective conductor, there must be an earth terminal in all insulated switch boxes, and also in metal switch boxes where there is not a solid conduit connection to the box and cover plate.

Every ceiling rose must also have an earthing terminal, and when three-plate ceiling roses (Fig. 4.1) are used for looping the phase wire, this terminal must be insulated so that it cannot be touched accidentally. Only one outgoing flexible cord may be attached, unless the rose is designed especially for multiple pendants.

It should be noted that the circuit protective circuit is not included in the wiring circuits shown in this chapter.

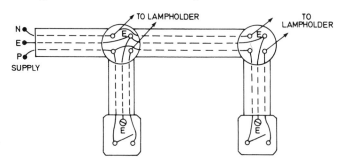

Fig. 4.1. Two light points separately switched, wired on the three-plate (four-terminal) ceiling rose system

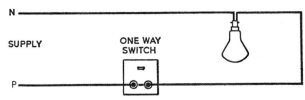

Fig. 4.2. One-way single-pole switch circuit

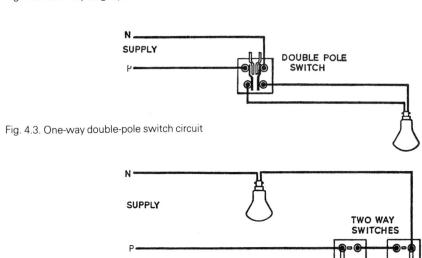

Fig. 4.3. One-way double-pole switch circuit

Fig. 4.4. Two-way switching

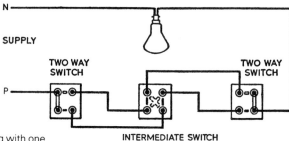

Fig. 4.5. Two-way switching with one
intermediate switch

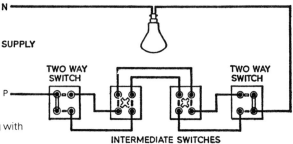

Fig. 4.6. Two-way switching with
two intermediate switches

Switch wiring

With the one-way circuit shown in Fig. 4.2 the single-pole switch must be connected in the phase, for if connected in the neutral the circuit is still alive up to the lamp point.

A double-pole switch may be included in the circuit (Fig. 4.3) to ensure that both conductors are completely isolated from the supply. The principal purpose of a double-pole switch is for the main control of circuits and the local control of cookers, water heaters, radiators and other fixed apparatus.

In principle, the two-way switch is a single-pole change-over switch. Inter-connected in pairs, two switches provide complete control from two positions and should therefore be installed in bedrooms, on landings and in long halls, on single-flight stairways and in any room with two doors. Fig. 4.4 shows the generally accepted method of wiring two-way circuits.

Simple two-way wiring is normally adequate for long halls, corridors and passage-ways with many doors, and multi-flight stairways. For safety and convenience every access point should have its own lighting control switch, provided economically and simply by installing intermediate switches. Any number of these can be introduced into a two-way circuit. Fig. 4.5 shows how a single intermediate switch should be connected when this is to be added to a two-way circuit. The method of interconnection for two or more intermediate switches is illustrated in Fig. 4.6.

The function of a master switch is to limit or vary the scope of control afforded by other switches in the same circuit. An example of a simple master control is shown in Fig. 4.7. The installation has each light controlled individually by a single-pole switch but there is a double-pole switch for master control of the installation as a whole. With such a master

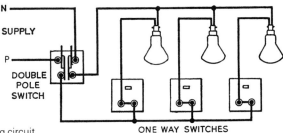

Fig. 4.7. Master control wiring circuit

switch near the main door to a house or flat, the residents have the facility for controlling all lights from one position. The master switch may be of a type for secret-key operation.

Another form of master switching, shown in Fig. 4.8, gives the user over-riding control of groups of lights independently of, and remote from the individual switches. The scheme allows for a policeman or a watchman to flood momentarily certain areas with light without having to operate several separate switches. The lights are controlled separately by two-way switches, and the common terminals are coupled to a single-pole master control device. This can be a switch or a bell-push with a retractive action,

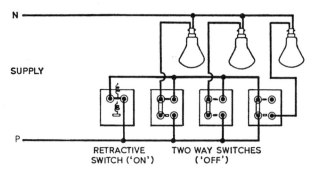

Fig. 4.8. Master wiring circuit for overriding control of groups of lights

i.e. a device that is effective only while it is held manually in the 'on' position. It should be noted that where 5 A switches are employed in such a circuit, the total connected load must not exceed 5 A.

The 'veto' master switch is a control device which is usually specified in the lighting circuits for the stairways of large hotels, restaurants, public buildings, theatres and other places where the unauthorized extinction of stair lights would endanger public safety and where complete two-way control is required by the staff. In the example shown in Fig. 4.9, a one-way switch has been introduced into a two-way circuit in such a way that it can be used to short-circuit the strapping wires and thus prevent the lights being extinguished from either of the two-way switches.

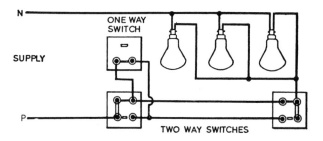

Fig. 4.9. 'Veto' master switching circuit

Fluorescent-lighting fittings

The wiring circuit of a fluorescent lighting fitting connects the tube with the items of control gear which are usually integrated into present-day fittings. However, if the main wiring circuits in use are understood it is much easier to discover defective components when a failure occurs.

A fluorescent tube cannot be used without control gear which includes a stabilizer or ballast to provide resistance or impedance in series with the tube to restrict or control the current to the correct value for stable operation. To ensure stability, the voltage applied across the tube and ballast in series must be at least 1.5 times the running voltage of the tube, e.g. a tube with a nominal running voltage of about 100 V a.c. will operate satisfactorily on a nominal 200 V a.c. supply.

In addition to the ballast, the control gear may include a starting device and capacitors to correct power factor or minimize radio and television interference. The various components may be combined together as a single unit or fitted separately in the lighting fitting.

A ballast could consist of a wire wound resistor but this would reduce overall efficiency due to the heat loss in the resistor. An incandescent filament lamp serves as a ballast and, supplementing the light from the tube, increases the overall efficiency. One type of fluorescent fitting has a starter ballast lamp comprising an incandescent lamp combined with a glow starter switch.

Some method of starting a tube is needed because the minimum voltage required for stable operation is not enough to start the discharge. The basic features of one type of starting circuit are shown in Fig. 4.10. The 'starter' is a switch which, when closed, enables current to flow through the choke and the two cathodes in series. As soon as the cathodes reach a

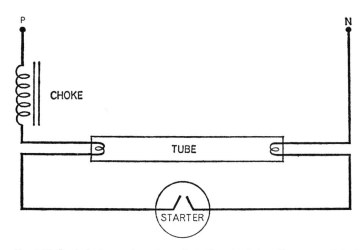

Fig. 4.10. Basic features of one type of starting circuit for a fluorescent light fitting

temperature at which electrons are emitted, local ionization is set up at each cathode and the ends of the tube begin to glow. The starter switch is then opened rapidly and, due to the self-inductance of the choke and the sudden change of current, there is an induced voltage pulse several times greater than the mains voltage which establishes the discharge.

Automatic starter switches allow a heating current to flow through the cathodes for a predetermined period before the switch opens to produce the striking pulse. The switches incorporate a small radio interference suppression (r.i.s.) capacitor.

Glowswitch starter circuit

In the glowswitch type of automatic starter, the switch contacts are mounted on bi-metallic strips which bend towards each other when heated. The contacts are sealed into a glass bulb, which is filled with argon gas, and the whole assembly, including the capacitor, is housed in a metal canister. The starter circuit is shown in Fig. 4.11.

When the circuit switch is closed, full mains voltage is applied across the starter switch and a glow of discharge is set up across the open contacts. The discharge heats the bi-metal strips, causing the switch to close, so that the pre-heating current flows. As the discharge is extinguished, the bi-metal strips start to cool. After a set period, the contacts spring apart and the voltage pulse is applied across the tube.

The r.i.s. capacitor discharges across the closing contacts and a slight welding action occurs. This tends to hold the contacts together as the bi-metal strips cool until the contacts finally part with a quick clean break.

Thermal-switch starter circuit

Although now generally obsolete, thermal switches are still in service on older fittings. In the circuit shown in Fig. 4.12, the switch contacts are mounted on bi-metal strips connected to terminals BD and a small heater coil is connected to terminals AC. The assembly is housed in a metal canister together with the r.i.s. capacitor.

When the circuit switch is closed, the starter switch contacts are closed and current flows through the choke, the heater coil and the tube cathodes. The heat from the coil acts on the bi-metal strips to open the switch after a preset period so that a voltage pulse is produced. After striking, the normal running current through the heater coil is sufficient to keep the switch contacts apart.

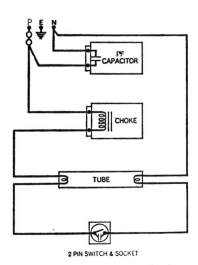

Fig. 4.11. Glowswitch starter circuit

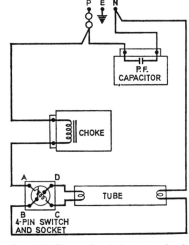

Fig. 4.12. Thermal-switch starter circuit

Double glowswitch starter circuits have been used for two short tubes (600 mm or 450 mm) operated as a series-pair, two starters being mounted in one canister. However, a later circuit uses two two-pin small canister switches, one connected across each tube as shown in Fig. 4.13.

Another circuit used earlier but now virtually obsolete comprises two tubes, one operating at 0.5 leading and one at 0.5 lagging power factor, so that the combined circuit power factor approaches unity. The leading power factor is obtained by means of a series capacitor.

Fig 4.14 shows the circuit of a 2400 mm 125 W tube which includes a series capacitor and a glowswitch starter.

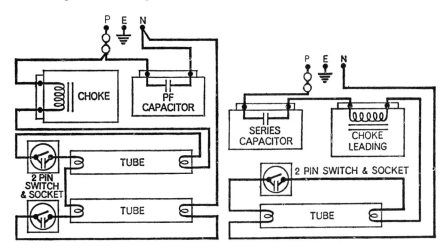

Fig. 4.13. Series-pair circuit with two two-pin glowswitches

Fig. 4.14. 2400 mm 125 W tube circuit with series capacitor and glowswitch starter

Electronic starters

These modern forms of starter switch are often termed *ignitors*. The majority are solid-state devices. While replacing the conventional glow starter they provide cathode heating in a similar manner. Ignitors make for instant starting with an extended lamp life. They have the advantage of operating at temperatures as low as $-5°C$ and so are eminently suitable for outdoor lighting.

Switchless start circuits

With the starter switch circuits, a second or two may elapse between switching on and the tube striking. With the switchless start circuits the starting period is minimized by arranging for the discharge to strike automatically as soon as the cathodes reach emission temperature.

Fig. 4.15 shows a switchless start circuit which uses the Thorn Quickstart unit and tube. The unit comprises an iron-cored auto-transformer with secondaries at each end which provide 10–12 V across each tube cathode when the 200–250 V supply is applied to the primary. The tube is so designed that if an earthed metal strip is mounted close to it (within 13 mm) along its entire length, striking will occur automatically. If the lighting fitting metalwork serves as the metal strip it is only necessary to earth the fitting. Once the arc has been established, the voltage across the tube (and also across the Quickstart unit) drops to about half mains voltage. Auxiliary cathode heating is therefore reduced automatically.

Fig. 4.16 shows the Quickstart circuits for a series-pair of 600 mm 40 W/20 W or 450 mm 15 W tubes.

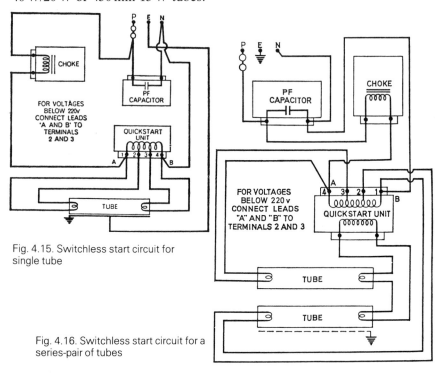

Fig. 4.15. Switchless start circuit for single tube

Fig. 4.16. Switchless start circuit for a series-pair of tubes

The starting and running sequence of the 2400 mm Quickstart circuits shown in Figs. 4.17 and 4.18 is based on the principle of resonant-start. During starting, about 350 V is applied across the tube due to the pre-heat current which flows through the transformer primary and secondary, the p.f. capacitor and the left-hand tube cathode (in the case of the 125 W circuit). The right-hand cathode is pre-heated by a separate winding on the transformer (both cathodes in the case of the 85 W ballast).

Once the tube has started, the tube current flows via the choke and the transformer primary windings. The current through the secondary and p.f. capacitor falls during the running period and the voltage across the tube cathodes is also reduced, thus improving tube life. The circuit harmonics and noise are lower than with normal 2400 mm gear and the power factor is almost unity.

Resonant start circuits have also been developed for use with 1500 mm 65 W and 1800 mm 85 W tubes (Fig. 4.19).

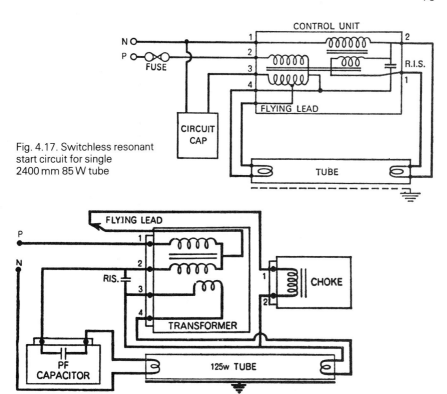

Fig. 4.17. Switchless resonant start circuit for single 2400 mm 85 W tube

Fig. 4.18. Switchless resonant start circuit for single 2400 mm 125 W tube

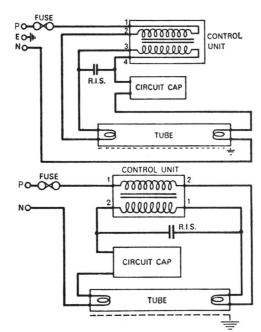

Fig. 4.19. Switchless resonant start circuits for 1500 mm 65 W tube. The two circuits have different ballast units. The top circuit is also suitable for an 1800 mm 85 W tube

Fig. 4.20 shows the twin-start circuit for two 2400 mm 85 W tubes of a new type with reduced gas pressure so that starting is easier and operating arc volts are lower. The cathode filament used in this tube has been designed to operate with a fixed 3.5 V of cathode heating. The single ballast unit is suitable for 230–240 V 50 Hz supplies and its connections are made directly to the mains and to the four lampholders.

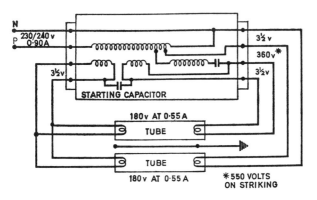

Fig. 4.20. Switchless twin-start circuit for two 2400 mm 85 W tubes

A starting voltage of about 550 V is applied across one tube through a small starting capacitor so initiating a glow discharge. The voltage impressed across the starting capacitor and the second tube in parallel establishes a glow discharge through the second tube. Both discharges are maintained in series until the cathode filaments reach emission temperature, when the discharge changes from the glow to the arc state. Both tubes then continue to operate, the series capacitor providing the necessary power factor correction for the inductance in the ballast.

The twin-start 85 W ballasts are not recommended for use in quiet locations. Earthed metalwork adjacent to the tubes is essential for reliable starting, and striking is satisfactory in ambient temperatures down to 5°C.

Fig. 4.21 shows a switchless start circuit for a 400 mm 40 W Quickstart circular tube.

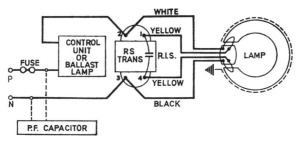

Fig. 4.21. Switchless start circuit for 400 mm 40 W circular tube

Dimming circuits

The obvious method of dimming a light would be by connecting a variable resistor in series with a tungsten lamp, but this is most clumsy and wasteful. Early attempts at improvement were made by use of a capacitor, but this method did not prove to be practical either. It had to wait until the advent of the thyristor or triac with appropriate triggering circuit before a satisfactory system could be adopted.

Fig. 4.22 shows a Thorn dimming circuit for three 1500 mm, 1200 mm or 900 mm tubes. The cathode heating transformer primary is connected

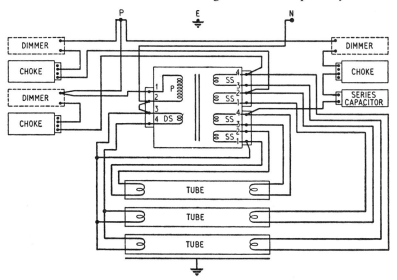

Fig. 4.22. Dimming circuit for three 1500 mm, 1200 mm or 900 mm tubes

across the main supply terminals so that the cathodes are supplied at an approximately constant 7 V, this voltage being independent of the tube current. A variable resistor is connected in series with each choke. Although most fluorescent dimming circuits include a cathode heating transformer, similar to that shown in Fig. 4.22, dimming control may be effected by an electronic scheme based on the thyristor.

D.C. control circuit

Fluorescent tubes and fittings with starter switch circuits can be used on 200–250 V d.c. supplies with slight circuit modifications. A typical circuit is shown in Fig. 4.23. The additional features of this circuit which are essential to the operation of the tube are a ballast resistance in series with the choke, a d.c. glow or thermal starter switch, and a reversing switch. The last item must be inserted in the circuit between the fitting and the supply to reverse the tube current periodically and thus prevent migration of the mercury to one end of the tube with a consequent loss of light. A special 1500 mm 80 W tube available has extra mercury to increase the period before migration occurs.

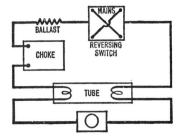

Fig. 4.23. Single-tube d.c. circuit for 900 mm,
1200 mm or 1500 mm tubes

Krypton filling

Argon-filled fluorescent tubes may with advantage be replaced by the
superior krypton triphosphor tubes for use on switch-start circuits with
glow-type starters. The triphosphors also result in a slower rate of
depreciation. The tubes are slimmer (26 mm diameter in contrast to the
usual 38 mm) although the standard bi-pin arrangement and dimension is
unaltered. There is an increased efficiency of 8 per cent in addition to
improved colour rendering.

Cold cathode lighting

Essentially a fluorescent tube with electrodes operating at much lower
temperatures than those of hot cathode tubes, the cold cathode type has a
life of 15 000 hours and starts instantly without delay or flicker as there is
no electrode pre-heat time. The easy starting is maintained over a wide
range of voltage fluctuation and life is relatively unaffected by the number
or frequency of switchings.

Typical circuits for cold cathode tubes are shown in Fig. 4.24. For
extensive installations the circuit shown in Fig. 4.24(a) is often used. With
three 2800 mm tubes connected in series, the supply voltage is stepped up
to provide about 3600 V for starting and 1900 V for normal running. The
transformer is designed to regulate automatically the secondary voltage so
that it falls to the running value as the tubes strike.

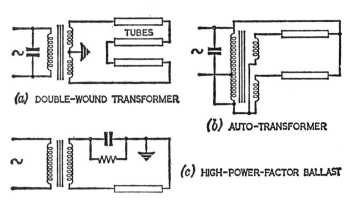

(a) DOUBLE-WOUND TRANSFORMER

(b) AUTO-TRANSFORMER

(c) HIGH-POWER-FACTOR BALLAST

Fig. 4.24. Typical circuits for cold cathode tubes

The auto-transformer connection (Fig. 4.24(*b*)) is designed to give a slim section and to provide each tube with an independent secondary winding so that in the event of a tube failure or a disconnection, the remaining tubes continue to operate. Up to four tubes can function from one auto-transformer. Fig. 4.24(*c*) shows a ballast for a single cold cathode tube. It will be noted that all three circuits include power factor correction capacitors.

Cold cathode installations can be dimmed by reducing the voltage applied to the transformers. Reduction to some 10–15 per cent of the maximum brightness can be achieved before a slight flicker occurs immediately before extinction.

Luminous locators

To reveal the position of switches, MK Electric Ltd. have developed luminous locators made to fit unobtrusively between the wall and the plate of flush accessories with 60.3 mm fixing centres. One of two types available, the neon locator emits in darkness a red glow above the switch or socket-outlet. The neon lamp is contained within a moulded ivory frame which matches other ivory accessories. The second type, the electro-luminescent locator, has a Panelume element. Contained within a transparent moulded frame, the electro-luminescent element in darkness emits a blue halo around the accessory.

Fig. 4.25 shows how the luminous locators are wired into one-way and two-way switch circuits.

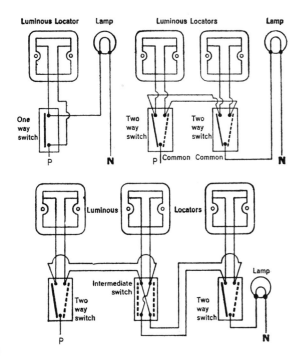

Fig. 4.25. Wiring circuits of MK luminous locators

Automatic time switches

Various types of time switch are used for the automatic control of lighting circuits when this is necessary for some special purpose. Certain types are designed specifically for lighting control but, in general, most time switches can be applied to the on/off switching of other circuits provided that the switching capacity is adequate and the required switching schedule can be obtained.

Time switch electrical circuits are fairly simple. Fig. 4.26 shows the basic circuit for on/off switching at preset times. The circuit switch is actuated mechanically in accordance with the setting of the 'hands' relative to the calibrated dial. With some time switches the hands are adjustable to positions appropriate for required timings but particularly for certain lighting applications there are time switches equipped with a solar dial. This type of switch is used for public and other lighting installations switched on at sunset and off at sunrise, the solar dial being calibrated to carry out an annual programme of on/off switching at the times relevant to the location of the installation.

Staircase lighting

As an economy measure, simple time-lag switches are often employed in buildings such as small hotels and blocks of flats. One pattern consists of a push-type switch causing a controlled release of air for a delay in switching off. They may be adjusted for a period up to 20 minutes. For safety, a further refinement is achieved by slow fading.

Wiring connections are shown in Fig. 4.27. It is of interest to note that light points and the time-lag switches are connected in parallel.

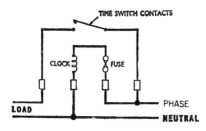

Fig. 4.26. Time-switch circuit for on/off switching at preset times

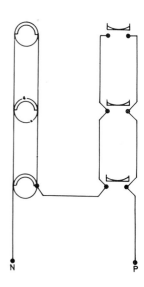

Fig. 4.27. Staircase or corridor control by pneumatic time-lag switches

Automatic changeover switch

Many varieties of time switch control are available for the installation
designer. Fig. 4.28 illustrates the circuit of the AMF/Venner T10 which
consists of a 24-hour time switch dial, fitted with two pairs of adjustable
tappets giving two 'on' periods per day (e.g. morning and evening). A
single 'on' period can easily be provided by simply disengaging one 'on'
and one 'off' tappet.

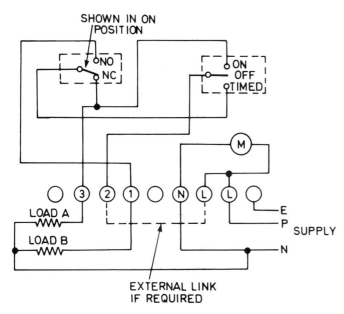

Fig. 4.28. AMF/Venner T10 15 A changeover time switch

The tappets which actuate a changeover microswitch lock positively in
position on the timing dial, giving complete protection against accidental
changes in their settings. The timing dial itself is driven from a self-starting
synchronous motor and is calibrated in half-hour intervals over the 24
hours.

An advance button enables the user to actuate the time-switch
mechanism manually, thus producing the next sequenced switching
condition in advance of the preset time. This advance facility will operate
at any time.

A further feature is provided by manual over-ride switches which include
an independent three-position switch having settings for 'on', 'timed' and
'off' conditions. By the use of this in conjunction with the timed settings a
flexible combination of automatic and manual control is readily available.

To facilitate installation the moulded base is fitted and wired first
without the encumbrance of the mechanism. The front casing can be
treated as a plug-on unit allowing easy removal for servicing without
disturbing the wiring.

'Wireless' light control

Switching by remote control with the Home Automation system (Fig. 4.29) requires no cables between the switch and lamp. The hand-held controller transmitter emits infra-red signals which are received by a ceiling-mounted or wall-mounted master. A press-button give a simple on, off or dimming

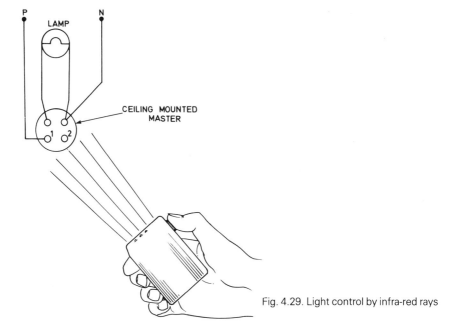

Fig. 4.29. Light control by infra-red rays

action by means of a single pulse. The infra-red rays will pass through glass with a range up to approximately 10 metres.

Further wall-mounted 'slave' units may be added by connection to terminals 1 and 2.

5 Heating control circuits

The simplest circuit involved in the control of space heating is one for the on/off switching of an electric heater. Additions to this elementary circuit are a room thermostat and/or a time switch to give some measure of automatic control with an overriding manual switching control to enable the heating to be selected either on or off regardless of what is called for by the automatic control.

The amount of automatic control applied to a space heating installation depends on its complexity and the extent to which the user is prepared to incur the relatively high cost of a fully automatic system. Certain controls are inherent in particular systems. Off-peak storage heating, for instance, is necessarily controlled to limit the period when it can be charged, and certain systems of warm air heating use controlled output fan-assisted storage units that can be either manually or automatically controlled.

Central heating systems using either oil or gas fired boilers necessarily include automatic features to ensure safe operation, but the control of space temperatures may be effected either manually or automatically. However, it has been established that, no matter what fuel may be used, to maintain a comfortable standard of space heating at minimum cost it is essential for the installation to be controlled automatically.

In general, heating schemes are designed to produce sufficient heat in the house to counteract the losses and to maintain the specified room temperature when the outside temperature is at the design minimum – usually $-1°C$. During the greater part of the heating season in the UK, the outside temperature is above this minimum and changes erratically daily or even hourly over a range of -4 to $18°C$, so the output of the heating installation must be varied accordingly.

It is not practicable to rely on manual adjustments to maintain required room temperatures for it results in under- and over-heating which cause discomfort while the latter also wastes fuel. In average conditions, an overshoot of only $1°C$ above a desired room temperature may increase fuel consumption by 10 per cent.

Automatic temperature controls can take into account changes in the weather, and the room temperatures can be selected and maintained as required. When it is unnecessary to heat all parts of a house to the same temperature all the time, with properly planned controls it is possible to have different levels appropriate to the particular room.

Thermostat principles

In general, the operating member of a metallic thermostat consists of a bi-metal strip or leaf of two metals with different thermal characteristics. When heat is applied to the strip, there is a movement in one direction, the amount of movement being approximately proportional to the change in temperature within certain limits.

The movement of the bi-metallic strip results in the operation of two contacts which are wired in series with the source of the heat energy, 'making and breaking' in accordance with the rise and fall of temperature. A device is incorporated to enable the thermostat to be adjusted at predetermined temperature limits.

To ensure that the contacts 'make and break' quickly and cleanly when the operating point is reached, a permanent magnet may be incorporated so that the contact movement may be accelerated. Also, for low current loadings, a small internal accelerating heating element may be fitted which assists in reducing temperature overshooting due to thermal delays. The accelerator heater may be left out of circuit if the current is high enough to cause sufficient self-heating to give the accelerating effect. Fig. 5.1 shows the construction of the thermostat, while Fig. 5.2 depicts how the thermostat may be employed to control large heating loads with the accelerating element incorporated in the circuit.

Air temperature control thermostats

An essential part of an automatic control scheme for space heating is the air thermostat used for on/off switching for the regulation of various units of the installation. Three types of air thermostat are illustrated diagramatically in Fig. 5.3. With the simple type (a) control is relatively ineffective because of the fairly large temperature swing involved in the on-off operation. The swing may be as much as 5°C.

In practice, if the thermostat is set to what is considered to be a comfortable temperature, there will be periods when the temperature is too low for comfort, due to the fall in ambient temperature that has to occur before the heating is switched on after having been switched off at the set temperature. As usually the periods of low temperature will not be tolerated, they will be avoided by setting up the thermostat such that there will be periods when the temperature is excessive – and both uncomfortable and costly.

To reduce the temperature swing of the simple type of thermostat it can be provided with 'thermal feedback' by the inclusion of an accelerating heater H1, shown in Fig. 5.3(b). When the thermostat makes contact on falling temperature, the heater is energized and supplies heat to the

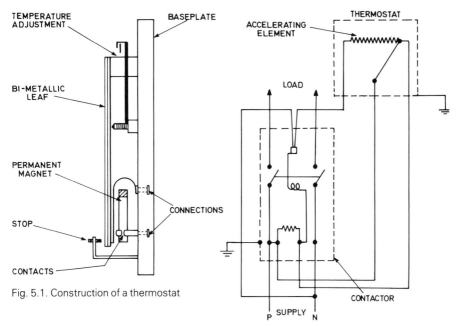

Fig. 5.1. Construction of a thermostat

Fig. 5.2. Use of a thermostat and contactor to control large heating loads, with the accelerating element in circuit

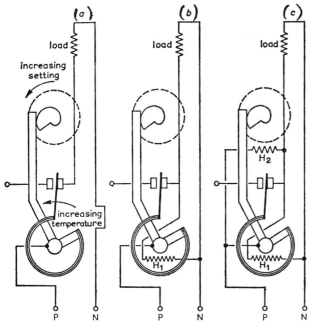

Fig. 5.3. Circuits of air thermostats: (a) simple type; (b) type with thermal feedback; (c) type with feedback and compensation

temperature sensitive element causing it to break circuit earlier than would otherwise be the case.

With an accelerating heater, the temperature swing may be reduced to a low value but unless the setting of the thermostat is altered, the mean room value will be lower in very cold weather than in mild weather. For close regulation, it is necessary to provide for the reduction or elimination of offset, that is the difference between the controlled temperature and the desired temperature at any load. Offset in a thermostat with thermal feedback is reduced or eliminated by the use of a second heater H2 called the compensating heater; see Fig. 5.3(c). It is energized when the thermostat is in the off position and its control action is such that with changing weather conditions it resets the control point to minimize offset.

Off-peak heating installations

Off-peak heating is invariably based on the heat-storage principle. During the night the heater stores up heat until either its thermostat operates or a time switch cuts off the supply. A cheap rate applies and there may be a mid-day boost. The four main methods are: unit block storage heaters, floor warming, air-duct heating, and the use of water as a storage medium.

The controlled type of block storage heater may be fan assisted, the fan being switched on when a rapid discharge of warm air is required to circulate round the room. The fan is connected to the normal unrestricted supply. Additional output control can be obtained by means of an adjustable damper. A room thermostat may be fitted and connected in the fan circuit to provide an automatic on/off cycle of operation throughout the day. As the temperature of the block falls, the fan runs for longer periods.

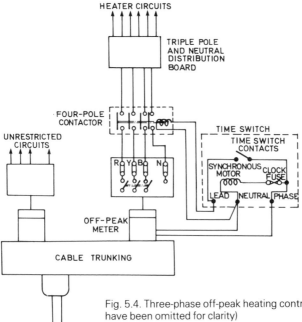

Fig. 5.4. Three-phase off-peak heating controls (meter tail connections have been omitted for clarity)

The room thermostat may be subject to the over-riding control of a time switch to bring the fan into action under thermostatic control at predetermined times during the day. The heater contains an adjustable input charge thermostat and, to prevent overheating, a thermal cut-out is included.

The newer Economy 7 tariff is operated by a meter having two sets of numerals and a time switch. However, off-peak wiring is separately metered and must constitute a completely distinct installation.

The general supply and consumer's control arrangement is shown in Fig. 5.4 – here the heaters are spread over three phases. There may be an additional consumer's time switch so as to operate only for part of the off-peak period.

Fig. 5.5 illustrates an alternative scheme that incorporates an external sensing unit (a sensor is a component which registers the actual conditions of the environment, e.g. air temperature, humidity, liquid temperature, pressure, flow).

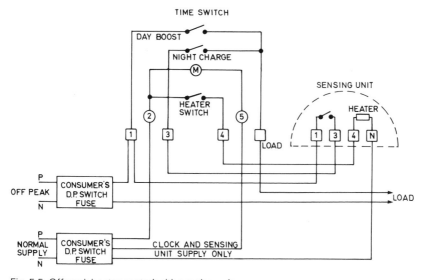

Fig. 5.5. Off-peak heater control with sensing unit

Time switch control

As already stated, for the on/off switching of some heating systems a time switch is used either by itself or in conjunction with a thermostat.

Fig. 5.6 shows the circuit of a small pushbutton-operated time switch suitable for controlling heating in waiting rooms, hotel bedrooms, stores and other places occupied at only irregular or intermittent intervals. Capable of controlling loads up to 3 kW, the timer is arranged to give a preset period of heating, say 30 minutes, when the pushbutton is pressed. At the end of this period the timer will switch the heater off and reset ready for the next operation. The change-over contact provides an extra terminal

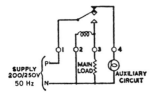

Fig. 5.6. Pushbutton-operated timer for control of heating unit

for controlling an auxiliary circuit if required, e.g. a signal lamp to be switched on when the main load is switched off or on.

Thermostatic control of heating equipment may be exercised either by a single device or by a combination of devices necessary to achieve precise regulation, together with manual controls and in some cases time switching.

Water heating

Immersion heaters are often misused, resulting in expensive energy wastage. Smith's Imerset (Fig. 5.7) is designed to eliminate this loss in heat energy. The unit provides for twice daily switching, plus an optional mid-day boost. Extra timesetting pins are available for multiple switching and a manual advance is incorporated.

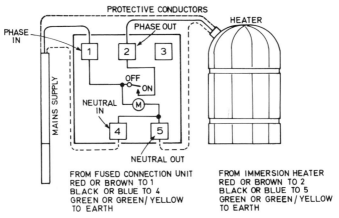

Fig. 5.7. Smith's immersion heater time switch (Imerset)

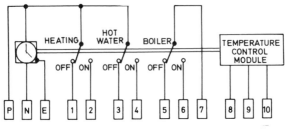

Fig. 5.8. Smith's 200 hot water and central heating controller

More versatile time switches are called 'programmers'. They possess a time switch with additional switches so that the domestic hot water supply can be separated from the central heating thus enabling different times to be selected for the two services.

An example is the Smith Controller 2000 (Fig. 5.8). It is an electronic quartz microprocessor-based central heating and hot water programmer giving the user slider-selection of once, twice, continuous or off for hot water and heating. The unit contains a built-in memory for prolonged mains failure. There is also an easy conversion from independent to gravity-flow systems.

The Satchwell Sunvic Plug-in Duoflow system offers an alternative programmer. It is designed for systems employing a common pump to serve both the heating circuit and domestic hot water requirements (Fig. 5.9). An actuator automatically switches hot water from the boiler to the central heating and hot water circuits or to either as required. When both heating and hot water services are at their preset temperature, the boiler and circulating pump are switched off.

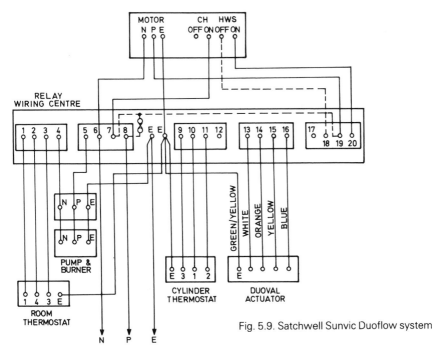

Fig. 5.9. Satchwell Sunvic Duoflow system

The same firm offers an Electronic Programmer ET1401 (Fig. 5.10). The basis of the ET is a single-chip microcomputer. It has four on/off periods during the 24-hour day, and controls either central heating or hot water or both functions. Any program set will automatically operate within the selected time period, unless manually changed. It is suitable for any domestic heating system incorporating a gas, oil or solid-fuel automatic boiler and can be used with most types of secondary controls, both on/off or modulating.

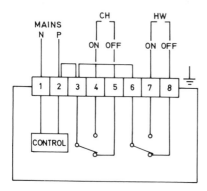

Fig. 5.10. Wiring diagram for a Sunvic ET 1401 programmer

A four-digit fluorescent green display provides time-of-day and time-period program information. The programmer is operated by pushbuttons and slide switches, with green indicators providing program information on hot water and central heating. Manual override is provided for continuous on or off for either central heating or hot water or both. In either position, the stored time periods are not disturbed, allowing the automatic program to resume once the override has been removed.

A 24-hour clock is controlled by the mains supply, and time of day is continuously displayed unless a program-setting operation is being performed. The brightness of the display means that it can be easily read from a distance, or in an unlit cupboard.

Other thermostats

The Satchwell Sunvic Room Thermostat TLX complies with test-house requirements in most countries, including BS 3955. It has either a single-pole single-throw (on/off) or single-pole double-throw (changeover) switch action (Fig. 5.11) as well as a robust magnetically controlled switch mechanism with contact rating either 2 A (changeover) or 6 A (on/off). A special fast-break switch action is installed to give long life and minimum radio and TV interference, and an accelerator heater is incorporated.

A microcomputer basic element is incorporated in the Satchwell Sunvic Electronic Clock Thermostat (Fig. 5.12). This thermostat can be programmed for up to four energy-saving periods in 24 hours. It controls room temperature at two levels, day and night (on and reduced) combining room temperature and time control.

A four-digit display indicates time of night and day, and can be called to display ambient temperatures and all programmed time periods and temperatures. The thermostat is operated by five pushbuttons with green indicators providing program information. Manual override is incorporated to allow independent time control of temperature to either day or night levels, and a day-omission facility gives omission up to six consecutive days in any seven-day period. The use of manual override or day omission will not disturb the stored time periods. Battery reserve with automatic recharging is also available on selected models.

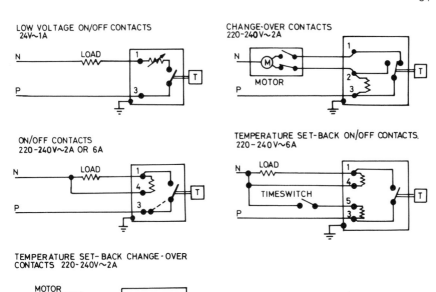

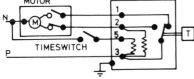

Fig. 5.11. Versions of the Sunvic TLX room thermostat

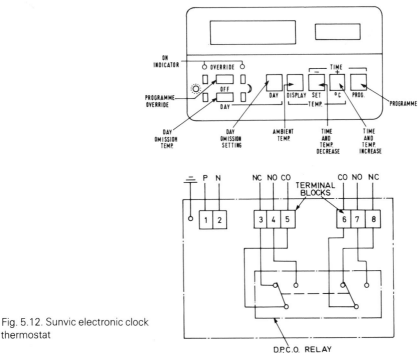

Fig. 5.12. Sunvic electronic clock thermostat

Off-peak storage heating schemes

As already described, the application of a thermostat regulates heat output from a hot water radiator installation by on/off switching of the water circulating pump. The heating of the whole house is controlled in accordance with the temperature in the vicinity of the room thermostat; but the controlled room temperature can be reduced to a lower level by manual adjustment of the thermostat òr by a time switch. Domestic hot water is supplied from the same thermostatically controlled boiler, at a temperature unaffected by heating requirements, to an indirect cylinder.

As a supplementary feature to the above scheme, a clamp-on thermostat is fitted to the hot water cylinder and connected to the heating circulating pump. The object is to achieve quick recovery of the water temperature in the cylinder after a large quantity of water has been drawn off. The pump is switched off whenever the temperature of the water in the cylinder falls below the setting of the clamp-on thermostat. There are two alternative methods of connecting the controls. With that shown in Fig. 5.13(a), the temperature of the water in the cylinder will be governed by the boiler thermostat.

With the connections shown in Fig. 5.13(b), firing control is transferred from the boiler thermostat to the cylinder thermostat whenever heating is not required, i.e. when the room thermostat is satisfied, thus allowing the water in the cylinder to be stored at a lower temperature that that of the water supplied to the radiators. If necessary, the heating can be resumed as soon as the cylinder water temperature has recovered. The setting of the boiler thermostat must be at least 11°C higher than that of the cylinder thermostat.

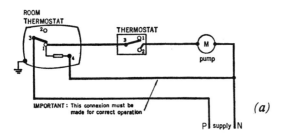

(a)

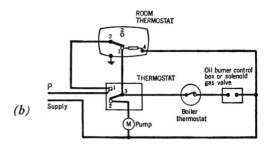

(b)

Fig. 5.13. Alternative circuits of control scheme including hot water cylinder thermostat

Heat pumps

An air-to-water heat pump (Fig. 5.14) system employs a fan to draw in outside air, which is then blown out again at a lower temperature. Heat taken from the air is used to raise the temperature of water, the water being made to pass through radiators of the conventional central heating system.

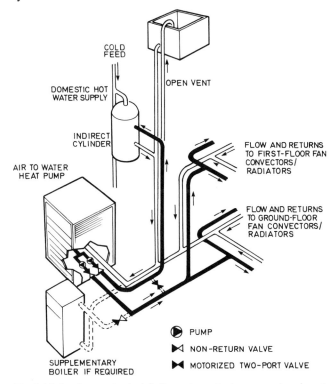

COLD FEED

OPEN VENT

DOMESTIC HOT WATER SUPPLY

INDIRECT CYLINDER

FLOW AND RETURNS TO FIRST-FLOOR FAN CONVECTORS/ RADIATORS

AIR TO WATER HEAT PUMP

FLOW AND RETURNS TO GROUND-FLOOR FAN CONVECTORS/ RADIATORS

● PUMP

◁ NON-RETURN VALVE

◀ MOTORIZED TWO-PORT VALVE

SUPPLEMENTARY BOILER IF REQUIRED

Fig. 5.14. An air-to-water installation using a dual pump system (courtesy Myson Ltd)

Heat pumps may be fitted in place of, or in conjunction with, oil, solid-fuel or gas boilers. Compared with an electric immersion heater element, they can add the same amount of energy to the water using one-half or one-third of the power by concentrating the low-grade heat of the atmosphere into heat at useful temperatures.

The action of heat pumps may be considered as the reverse of refrigerators, which take heat from the cold interior compartment and lose heat at the back. It is important to note that heat can be extracted from a variety of agents such as air, groundsoil or water. For operation, the only energy necessary is electricity to drive the induction-pump motor and fan. By the provision of a heat-store tank lined with glassfibre insulation, advantage can be taken of a night-rate tariff.

Adaptations of the air-to-water heat pumps make them usable for air-to-air air conditioning. This reversing process cools during hot days and can bring warmth when the weather is cold. The integrated heating/cooling system brings all-year comfort, such comfort depending upon correct temperature, humidity and air purity. The atmospheric control by programmed automatic methods is an advance on simple ventilation. Essential components to provide comfortable conditions are dust filters, humidity controllers and some form of silencer. Typical dust filters are electrostatic in action and in conjunction with pre-filter traps clear tobacco smoke, dust and dirt odours, pollen and certain bacteria. Contaminated air is drawn from the room and dust particles are given a positive charge. They are then attracted to metal plates and held on to the surfaces until removed by washing.

Heat pumps are usually fitted outdoors, sometimes to an external wall, but may be roof-mounted or even in a cellar where available. An enterprising development uses a wall-mounted indoor fan coil with a microcomputer remote-control panel, permitting normal or automatic operation and incorporating a 12-program timer.

Shower heating

A Cortina Electric single-pole time switch plus a built-in relay (Fig. 5.15) is used for applications where a delay may be required between the insertion of a coin and the operation of the appliance or where the operating point is some distance from the meter position. A common use for this type of control is where solenoid valves are required to dispense hot water (e.g. shower units and sink heaters). Remote control is achieved by a pushbutton or bell-pull at a point convenient to the consumer, who can then switch on the appliance safely at any point after the insertion of a coin (7.5 A or 15 A).

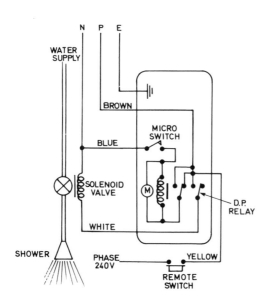

Fig. 5.15. Shower water heating

A single-pole time switch is fitted in conjunction with a 30 or 45 A built-in contactor for applications where a large-capacity switch is required. If supplied with a credit saver (Fig. 5.16) it affords greater economy and convenience to the consumer and saves the installation of an external switch and wiring. Suitable applications include supplies to flats and rooms, under-floor heating, etc.

Heavy heating controls

Conrad and Ridout CRL power switches are intended for controlling heavy resistive heating loads. They are not suitable for controlling such loads via the primary of a three-phase transformer, but may drive such loads via the primaries of three separate single-phase transformers.

Full synchronization, in the zero-switching or phase-angle mode, can only be achieved by two load configurations. They are commonly described as three-wire and open delta (Fig. 5.17).

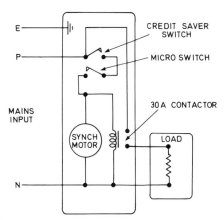

Fig. 5.16. Contactor control for a shower

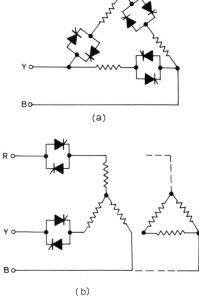

Fig. 5.17. Conrad and Ridout heavy resistive heating load controls: (a) open-delta; (b) three-wire

Storage heating

The early uncontrolled type of block storage heater contained a wire-wound element embedded in fireclay, concrete or similar material having a high thermal capacity for storing heat and enclosed in a metal casing. The Supertone Dimplex EC storage heater (Fig. 5.18) uses a remote electronic temperature sensor which monitors room temperatures during the charge period according to the heat losses from the room and is designed to take maximum advantage of an off-peak tariff.

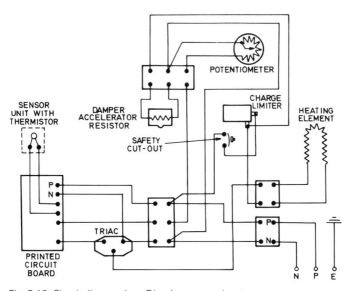

Fig. 5.18. Circuit diagram for a Dimplex storage heater

To perform this function most satisfactorily it is essential that the heater is correctly sized for the room. In addition to the automatic charge-input control, there is a variable output control which enables the user to select an earlier or later boost of additional heat, the amount depending upon the charge taken by the heater.

There are two control knobs, input and output. The input control knob is used to pre-select the room temperature at the end of the charge period. The user may programme the electronic room temperature sensor to relate charging of the heater to room temperatures of between 5°C and 65°C.

The output control consists of a bimetal activated damper mechanism which releases available extra heat from the core as required. The user may advance or retard the release of available heat by adjusting a rotary control knob.

6 Indicator and alarm circuits

Many of the different types of indicator and alarm circuits used in various classes of premises are basically similar to the simple scheme shown in Fig. 6.1. In this scheme each of the circuits to the indicator may be closed either by a push or a switch, or by the contacts of a fire detection device. The indicator may be either a drop-flag or a luminous type fitted with a reset device to cancel signals as required. A battery is used to power the system

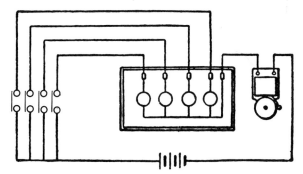

Fig. 6.1. Basic indicator and alarm scheme

when continuous availability is essential. Alternatively, the battery may be used as a standby to a rectified a.c. mains supply, or may be trickle-charged to ensure continuity of supply. When the system is not an essential service, it may be energized from the mains through a step-down transformer.

In a system with long runs of wire, the alarm device will be energized by the closing of a relay with an operating coil which is sensitive to much smaller current than that required to operate the alarm. With the simple arrangement shown in Fig. 6.2, the relay coil requires for operation only one-half of the voltage needed for the bell.

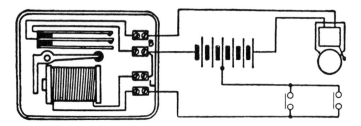

Fig. 6.2. Relay-operated bell circuit

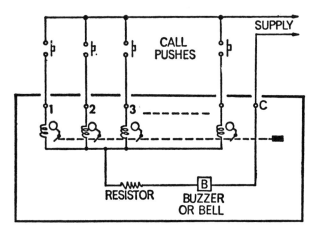

Fig. 6.3. Drop-flag indicator system where alarm sounds only when the push is pressed

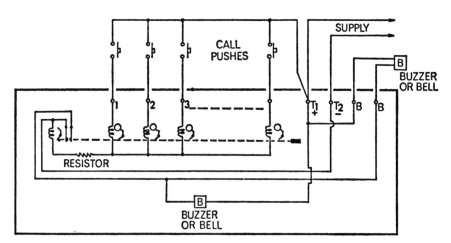

Fig. 6.4. Drop-flag indicator system where the alarm relay is reset with the signals

Drop-flag indicator systems

The wiring circuits of a calling system depend on such factors as the service that has to be provided and the number and location of the calling points and the receiving centre. These factors determine the type of indicator, alarm and other facilities required.

Fig. 6.3 shows a simple system based on a drop-flag indicator and an alarm that sounds only while the call push is being depressed. If additional alarms are required to operate when the push is pressed, a self-restoring relay must be fitted in the indicator (Fig. 6.4). If the sound signal must be maintained until reset at the indicator, a hand replacement relay must be included in the indicator. This can be reset either by the indicator reset knob or by a separate reset knob (Figs 6.4 and 6.5). The advantage of the latter is that the sound signal can be cancelled while leaving the signal or signals displayed.

Personal call system

Apart from calling systems covering extensive areas, there are local systems that enable a person in a private room to instruct callers as to if and when they are available. Fig. 6.6 shows the circuits of an executive's signal indicator set used to instruct callers. On the desk are three pushbuttons for

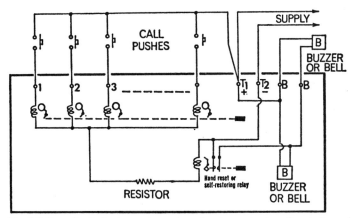

Fig. 6.5. Drop-flag indicator system where the alarm relay is self-restoring or hand reset independently from the signals

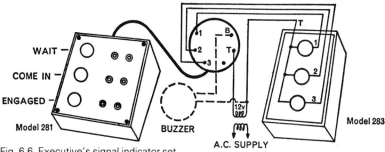

Fig. 6.6. Executive's signal indicator set

setting the corresponding signal on the unit outside the door. Operation of the pushbutton illuminates the outside signal and also a monitor signal on the desk fitting to prevent signals being left on or overlooked. Each signal has a separate cancelling button. The corresponding desk fitting and outside lamps are connected in series so that there is an immediate indication of a failure of an outside lamp. The desk fitting is equipped with overpress contacts for operating a buzzer if required.

Luminous call systems

Call systems using light signals have several advantages over the ordinary bell or drop-flag system. They are particularly suitable for calling for the services of staff in hospitals, hotels and ships.

With the system, pressing a calling push illuminates a light signal in the central service or duty-room, indicating that service is required in a particular area. Additional to this light signal is a corresponding light signal adjacent to the initiating point, to indicate the actual position from which the call originated – sometimes called a 'reassurance' lamp.

Other light signals are arranged at convenient points, e.g. in corridors, so that any additional calls can be traced and attended to immediately, by following the appropriate lights and without staff having to return to the duty-room to find the location of additional calls. This is a valuable feature to provide for the occasions when no one is present in the duty-room.

Signals can be cancelled only by pressing a reset button located at or near the initiating point. This ensures that the staff must answer the call before it can be cancelled. Where required an extension master indicator can be provided in the system to enable a supervisor to monitor the number of calls made and detect any delays in answering.

Fig. 6.7 shows a luminous call system for a hospital, which has both small and large wards that necessitate the proper utilization of the services of nursing staff to minimize effort while ensuring efficient attention to the needs of patients. With the system shown these objectives are achieved regardless of whether the wards are single, multi-bed or a combination of all types.

Where a simple but comprehensive scheme is required for single bed or small wards and bathrooms, each bed or bathroom can be provided with a calling push only, with a lamp and reset unit installed outside the ward or bathroom. Alternatively, each bed in either small or large wards can be provided with a calling push with its corresponding indicating lamp and reset unit. The second arrangement has the advantage that the patient has a definite indication that the call has been established, and the nurse knows (where there is more than one bed) exactly which patient has called for attention.

The pressing of the calling push illuminates a lamp in the indicator in the duty-room to show the area from which the call originated. Staff attending the call are guided by a lamp indicator outside the ward requiring service. Where necessary, other indicators can be positioned in corridors, etc., to help location of the ward. On arriving at the ward, the nurse presses the reset button which immediately cancels all signals connected with that call.

If further calls are initiated while a previous call is being attended, the appropriate bed (or ward), section and duty-room indicator lamps are illuminated for the information of staff already present.

Fig. 6.8 shows a single-service luminous call system for an hotel. Each guest-room has a call push and a combined lamp and reset unit outside the room. Alternatively, a reset unit inside the room with a lamp unit outside the door could be used.

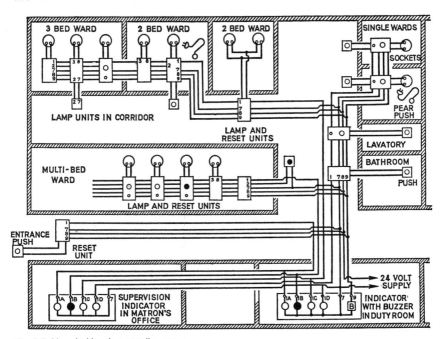

Fig. 6.7. Hospital luminous call system

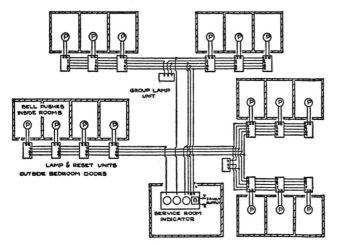

Fig. 6.8. Hotel single-service luminous call system

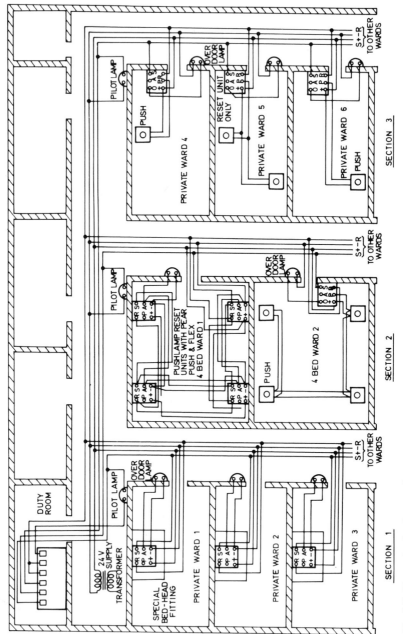

Fig. 6.9. Alternative luminous call system

The system may be divided into a number of groups or sections, comprising a number of rooms, and a lamp indicator is fitted in a position where it can be seen at the approach to each group or section. An indicator with a signal for each floor is located in the staff-room. The facilities provided are similar to those with the hospital system. Additional facilities that can be provided include a choice of two services; audible signals given only while the calling push is pressed; and repeat and master indicators.

Fig. 6.9 shows an alternative luminous call system. In section 1 a push-lamp reset system is fitted by each bedside, operating in conjunction with an overdoor lamp unit outside and one common group lamp in the main corridor. In section 2, multi-bed Ward No. 1 is equipped with a pushlamp reset system at each bed, operating in conjunction with an overdoor unit outside, but in Ward No. 2 pushes only are fitted beside the beds, working with one common reset unit inside and an overdoor lamp unit outside. Section 3 shows a call push only at each bed, with reset unit inside and overdoor lamp outside each ward. It should be noted that in all sections each call can only be cancelled inside the ward concerned.

Hotel bell systems

Hotel bell communication systems usually include a master indicator board (Fig. 6.10). Tracing out the circuits shows that when a push is pressed, in addition to the indication on the board of the floor concerned and a bell ringing on this floor, the master indicator records the floor where the call has originated.

Fire alarm systems

An individual scheme is required to provide effective means of giving warning of fire in particular premises but, in general, the scheme will involve either an open-circuit or closed-circuit system.

With many open-circuit systems (e.g. Figs. 6.11 and 6.13), the alarm initiating points are connected in parallel so that when they are actuated the circuit is completed to sound the alarm. While giving adequate cover, this type of system employs the minimum amount of equipment to suit the particular situation, but if full mains voltage is used to operate the system, the cable must be of the appropriate grade with adequate sheathing.

A closed-circuit system (Fig. 6.12) is advisable where the number of alarm initiating points to be used is much greater than the number of alarm signals. This necessitates extensive wiring between points and so it may be advantageous to use lower grade, less costly wiring for the actuating circuit.

However, the lower grade wiring should not be used for the alarm signal circuit. The alarm initiating points are connected in series and the circuit is opened when an alarm initiating point is operated, thus actuating the alarm via a relay.

This circuit is under test continuously so that if an open-circuit fault occurs, although a false alarm is given automatically, it draws attention to

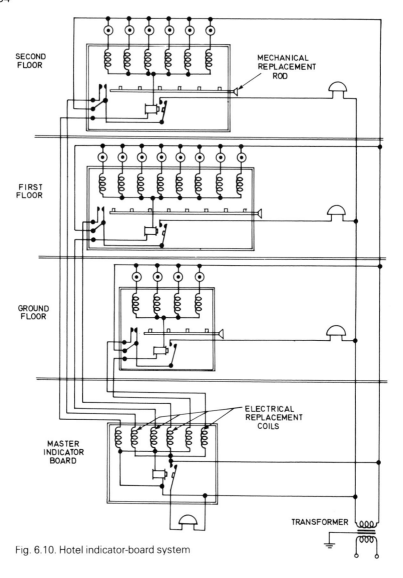

SECOND
FLOOR

MECHANICAL
REPLACEMENT
ROD

FIRST
FLOOR

GROUND
FLOOR

ELECTRICAL
REPLACEMENT
COILS

MASTER
INDICATOR
BOARD

TRANSFORMER

Fig. 6.10. Hotel indicator-board system

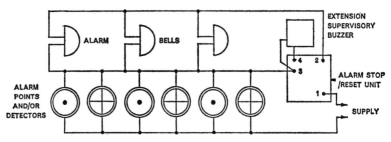

ALARM

BELLS

EXTENSION
SUPERVISORY
BUZZER

ALARM
POINTS
AND/OR
DETECTORS

4   2

3

ALARM STOP
/RESET UNIT

1

SUPPLY

Fig. 6.11. Open-circuit fire alarm system with alarm stop/reset unit

the circuit failure. If a grade of cable is to be used for the actuating circuit which is not suitable for full mains voltage, a transformer should be used to enable the circuit to be operated on 24 V, while the alarm signal circuit is operated, with appropriate cable, on the full mains voltage.

Fig. 6.11 shows the simplest open-circuit system for small premises which meets statutory requirements. Manually actuated points or automatic fire detectors are used to initiate the alarm. The system can be operated by mains voltage (derived from the supply side of the main switch) or from a low voltage source, either 24 V a.c. from a transformer or, preferably, 12 V or 24 V d.c. from trickle-charged accumulators.

The alarm stop/reset unit shown in Figs. 6.11 and 6.12 has a special function. When an alarm has been given, it is required to silence the audible alarm after a suitable period, particularly where trickle-charged accumulators are used. A normal switch is not permitted as it may be left in the 'off' position. The inclusion of the alarm stop/reset unit enables the

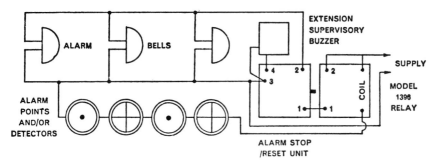

Fig. 6.12. Closed-circuit fire alarm system with alarm stop/reset unit

alarm to be silenced by pressing a button which diverts the current from the general alarm to a supervisory buzzer or lamp; but when the alarm initiating point has been restored to normal (e.g. the broken glass replaced) the alarm stop/reset unit immediately restores the circuit to its fully operative condition, and silences the supervisory buzzer or extinguishes the lamps.

In some buildings the location of a fire must be known immediately at a central point. This can be done by including an indicator in the system so that each alarm initiating point or group of points is connected to a separate signal on the indicator. Fig. 6.13 shows a system including a drop-flag type of indicator. An indicator of the luminous signal type can be used but the drop-flag type is to be preferred as it complies with the British Standard Code of Practice (Electrical Fire Alarms).

The number of signals on the indicator will depend, for example, on the number of floors or departments in the building. The alarm bells will be set off automatically and the indicator signal will operate when an alarm iniating point is operated. The bells can be silenced when required but the supervisory signal continues to operate and the indicator cannot be reset until the alarm initiating point has been restored to normal.

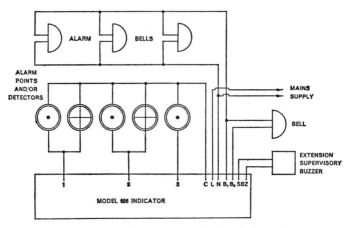

Fig. 6.13. Open-circuit fire alarm system with drop-flag indicator

Fire alarm control panel

The circuit of a Gent single zone fire alarm control panel is shown in Fig. 6.14. This is designed to comply with BS 3116 Part 4 (Automatic Fire Alarm Systems in Buildings) and can be used in systems installed to BS 5839 Part 1 (Fire Detection and Alarm Systems in Buildings), the Code of Practice for installation and servicing.

With all zone and sounder circuits monitored the unit is also self-contained, incorporating: fire alarm control circuits, fire signal, fault signal, batteries and charger, and reset push.

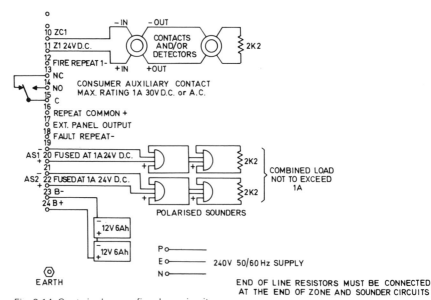

Fig. 6.14. Gent single-zone fire alarm circuit

There is a facility to allow for two separate sounder circuits, provided the total load does not exceed 1 A, for example 20 bells with a current consumption of 0.05 A each. The sounder can be set to generate a variety of sound signals, an intermittent tone, a sweep tone or a warble tone, and it has a remote-control facility to be operated from an extension switch.

Two sealed lead-acid batteries provide a nominal 24 V, 6 Ah capacity. A standby period of 84 hours is allowed for in the event of a mains failure, after which the batteries are capable of operating the alarm sounders for up to half an hour. In general the batteries have a recharge period of 24 hours depending upon the ambient temperature.

The accompanying sounders may have a sound output of 102 dBA at 1m with a voltage of 50 V d.c. and a current of 0.03 A, or 92 dBA at 3 m with a voltage of 50 V d.c. and a current of 0.03 A or a sound output at a rated voltage with a p.d. of 200/250 V and an a.c. current of 0.03/0.04. Fig. 6.15 shows some circuits for sound options of steady, sweep, warble or interrupt. Any of these sound options may be switched to steady by linking 'remote' to the negative supply.

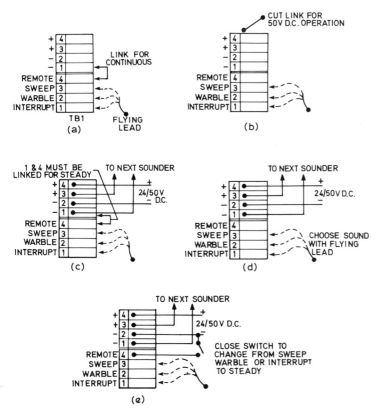

Fig. 6.15. Circuits for sound options of Gent sounder: (a) mains connections; (b) general connections; (c) connections for steady; (d) connections for sweep, warble, interrupt; (e) remote control of sound

Central bank system

A Chloride Gent fixed extinguishing system may be used for total flooding to protect areas normally occupied by personnel. This central bank system is based upon the principle that a hazard may be protected on a total flooding basis by one or more cylinders of halon manifolded together to a battery which feeds a carefully engineered distribution-pipe system (Fig. 6.16).

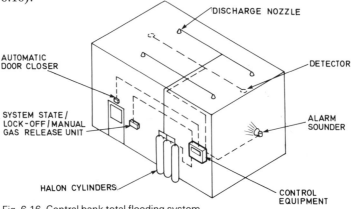

Fig. 6.16. Central bank total flooding system

To ensure a ten-second discharge, in particular when the cylinders are to be sited some distance from the area protected, each cylinder is super-pressurized with nitrogen to 43 bar (1 bar = $100\,000\,\text{N/m}^2$).

Distribution pipework and discharge nozzle sizes are calculated by a computer programmer. The use of multi-storage cylinders and selector valves permit the individual protection of more than one area from a single group of cylinders. Each cylinder is equipped with manual discharge facilities.

Remote operation of the system is provided by fitting a cylinder valve with a pressure-operated actuator for pneumatic release, a single-shot actuator for electrical release, or a mechanical actuator for pull-wire release. The cylinder valve is pneumatically operated, provided directly from the cylinder when a built-in pilot check valve is opened. The valve also includes a pressure-gauge/pressure-switch connection and a safety burst disc assembly.

When a system comprises more than one cylinder, the additional cylinders are fitted with pressure-operated actuators, interconnected by high-pressure hoses to the first cylinder valve actuator, such that all valves open simultaneously.

The cylinder valve outlets are connected by flexible high-pressure hoses to a common manifold which releases the halon into the distribution pipework system.

Detectors are usually arranged, two circuits to each protected zone. A fire condition is required on each circuit of detectors (double knock) before the panel confirms the fire condition. A coincident circuit then actuates the halon discharge cycle. Safeguards should be included.

Smoke/fire detector

The Gent equipment uses a photelectric beam system to detect smoke and air turbulence due to heat, and is suitable for inclusion as a detector in any protection system. Unlike point smoke detectors, which require smoke to penetrate into a chamber, the unit is capable of detecting smoke over its entire beam length, 90 m maximum. A meter on the control unit makes it possible to set the system to generate an alarm at a chosen level of obscuration dependent on the beam length used and the risk condition.

The equipment (Fig. 6.17) will also detect a smokeless fire by monitoring the changes in refraction caused by random movement of the heated air.

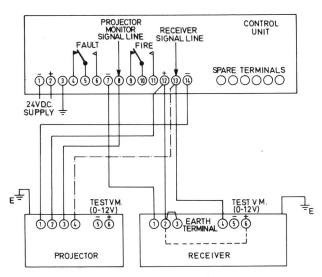

Fig. 6.17. Gent smoke/fire detector connections

The control unit has separate setting controls for heat and smoke detection. The setting meter can be switched individually to these systems to set it up. On sites that are unsuitable for the heat-detection system, such as heat-treatment plants etc., an internal switch allows this facility to be inhibited.

A time-delay circuit of approximately ten seconds is provided to avoid false alarms due to transient interruptions of the photoelectric beam. The system also includes a circuit to monitor the projector output and provide a relay contact which operates in the case of projector failure.

The complete circuit equipment includes a control unit which is designed to operate from a nominal 24 V d.c. supply and consumes less than 100 mA. It is eminently suitable for use with power packs, having a battery standby facility.

7 A.C. motors and control gear

The circuits involved in the control of an a.c. motor vary widely according to the operational duty of the motor, which is also a major factor determining the choice of a type of motor for a particular drive. The initial control requirement is that the motor must be started by connecting it to the supply, using a method appropriate to the type of motor and its rated power.

In addition to providing for starting, the control gear for induction motors may include devices for protection against overloads, faults, supply failure and single phasing and (when required) the means for speed variation, reversal and braking. For particular industrial drives, the control gear circuitry will also include items such as emergency controls and automatic control and interlocking devices.

In general, most of the control equipment for induction motors up to 600 V is of the air-break contactor type which is especially suitable for schemes requiring remote and automatic control features.

Direct-on-line starting

Most a.c. motors are started by one of several well-known methods. The simplest method is direct-on-line switching which is used whenever practicable for the squirrel-cage induction motor. The method enables the motor to develop maximum starting torque but with a current input of from six to eight, or sometimes ten times full load current. There are motors specially designed to start direct-on-line with only about three times full-load current.

The basic equipment for the direct-on-line starting of squirrel-cage motors is shown in Fig. 7.1. The circuit is such that with the isolator closed, the contactor closing coil is energized when the start button is pushed. An auxiliary contact on the contactor is arranged to maintain continuity of the control circuit after the start button has opened on release. A late-make and early-break auxiliary contact on the isolator provides an electrical interlock in the contactor control circuit.

The use of direct switching is restricted by the supply authorities who specify a maximum power to avoid disturbances to the public system. Also, direct switching is not suitable for motors driving high inertia plant where the acceleration time is so long that the starting current is maintained at a value which would operate the overload devices.

When the power of a squirrel-cage motor is too great to permit direct switching, it is necessary to use one of the methods that reduces the current at starting by applying a reduced voltage. With these methods the starting torque is also reduced considerably.

Primary resistance starting

Fig. 7.2 illustrates the method of starting by inserting resistance in the primary lines to the motor. Initially, the three-pole contactor M is closed to introduce the resistors into the lines, three-pole contactor R being open. After the motor has accelerated to near full speed, R is closed to short-circuit the resistors.

The method gives a smooth acceleration as the voltage across the motor terminals increases, and the line current decreases automatically as the motor speed increases. When first switched on the motor draws a heavier current than is the case with star-delta or auto-transformer starting; and as the resistors are in the primary lines they must be rated to carry this current for the time they are in circuit.

If required, tappings can be provided on the resistors so that the most suitable values may be determined on trials; or by adding further contactors, successive sections of the resistors can be short-circuited as the motor accelerates.

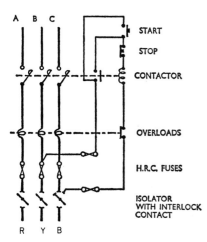

Fig. 7.1. Direct-on-line starting

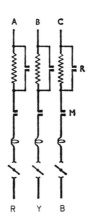

Fig. 7.2. Primary resistance starting

Star-delta starting schemes

For star-delta starting of a squirrel-cage motor both ends of each stator winding must be brought out to accessible terminals for connection to the control unit. This enables the windings to be connected in star initially and then reconnected in delta after the motor has accelerated to nearly full speed. With the motor connected in star, the applied voltage per phase is 57.7 per cent of the line voltage; and the current taken from the line is one-third of that which would be taken with direct switching.

Fig. 7.3 shows the basic primary connections and the detailed circuits. Three contactors are used, one being a triple-pole unit in the line, the other two being for connecting the windings in star and delta. It should be noted that the star contactor need only be double-pole. On closing the start

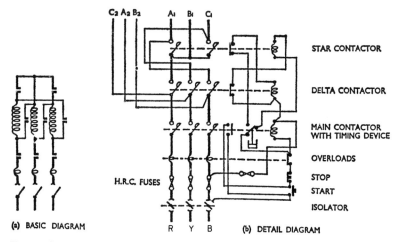

Fig. 7.3. Star-delta starting

button the main and star contactors close simultaneously to connect the motor to the supply. When the motor is nearly at full speed, the star contactor opens and the delta contactor closes and full voltage is applied to each phase. This change-over is achieved automatically by means of a timing device which is operated by the main contactor and is adjustable over a time period of, for instance, 0–20 seconds.

At the instant of change-over from star to delta, the motor is disconnected temporarily from the supply and there is a slight loss of speed. When the delta contactor closes, there will be some degree of current surge similar to that which occurs with direct switching. For this reason, h.r.c. fuses used to provide back-up protection must be rated to ensure that they do not operate. The magnitude of this current rush is minimized by allowing the motor to reach the maximum speed possible in star before changing over.

The star and delta contactors must be interlocked both electrically and mechanically to ensure that it is impossible for both to close together since this would cause a short-circuit.

A modified form of star-delta starter, the Wauchope starter, avoids current transients by the introduction of resistance when changing from the star to the delta connection. Not only does this avoid disconnecting the motor from the supply during the change-over, it also provides an additional accelerating step.

The arrangement of the circuits and the starting switching sequence are shown in Fig. 7.4. At step 1 the motor is connected in star to the supply, then during step 2 a resistance is connected in parallel with each phase of the motor winding, which is still connected in star. The step 2 arrangement

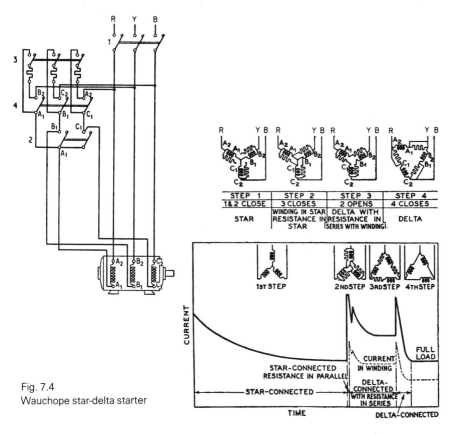

Fig. 7.4
Wauchope star-delta starter

is only maintained for a fraction of a second during which the line current is increased by the current flow through the resistor while the current through the winding remains the same. At step 3 the star point of the winding is open and this has the effect of connecting the motor windings in delta with a resistor in series with each phase. Finally, at step 4 the resistors are short-circuited and the motor is connected to the supply in delta.

Apart from the advantage of preventing transient current peaks, the Wauchope method also enables the motor to develop a continuous torque during the starting period without any loss in speed during the change-over from star to delta.

Auto-transformer starting

As the cost of the control equipment is relatively high, auto-transformer starting is seldom used for small motors. The auto-transformer has a number of tappings to provide for reduced voltage starting. The tappings are usually arranged to give voltages of 50, 60 and 75 per cent of line voltage, the tapping chosen being that which best suits the starting conditions. While other tappings can be provided, with tappings less than 50 per cent the torque developed by the motor is usually insufficient.

Fig. 7.5 shows two basic schemes, (a) and (b), for auto-transformer starting, and in (c) the detailed circuits for scheme (b).

The scheme (a) is simple requiring only the five-pole contactor S and the three-pole contactor R. Operation of the start button closes contactor S. After a time delay to allow the motor to accelerate on reduced voltage, contactor S opens and contactor R closes to put the motor on full voltage. The timing device is adjustable to suit the accelerating period for the particular drive. With this scheme there is a momentary disconnection of the motor from the supply during the change-over which may result in electrical stresses on the end-turns of the auto-transformer.

With the so-called Korndorffer method shown in Fig. 7.5(b) the motor remains connected to the supply without interruption, part of the auto-transformer acting as a choke during the transition period. It involves the use of the three-pole contactor S1 and the two-pole contactor S2 for starting and the three-pole contactor R for running. Initially, contactors S1 and S2 close to start the motor on the selected voltage tapping. After an acceleration period, the timing relay functions to open contactor S2 and to close R. The closing of R automatically causes S1 to open and the motor now runs on full voltage.

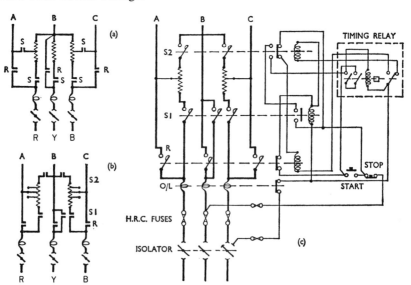

Fig. 7.5. Auto-transformer starting: (a) plain method; (b) Korndorffer method; (c) detailed circuits for (b)

Although not shown in the diagram some schemes include a further timing device which is so connected and timed that it opens the start contactors if for any reason the change-over to the run contactor has not occurred within a predetermined period. This is a safety precaution to prevent the motor inadvertently being left running continuously on the voltage tapping.

Slip-ring motor starting

To avoid starting difficulties due to the operation of overload trips the slip-ring motor is used. For starting, the rotor windings are connected to a starter incorporating three adjustable resistance elements. As the motor accelerates the resistance is reduced and finally short-circuited so that the motor is then running as an ordinary squirrel-cage type.

When starting a slip-ring motor with external resistance in the rotor circuit, the resistance is cut out in a series of steps as the motor accelerates. The number of steps is determined by the permissible variations in torque during the starting period. In general, the number ranges from three to seven. Basic and detailed diagrams for a typical three-step starter are shown in Fig. 7.6. Three contactors are used, one three-pole in the stator circuit and two two-pole in the external resistor circuit. The latter are usually designated rotor or accelerating contactors and their operation is controlled by automatic timing devices.

In certain cases it may be economical to use a three-pole contactor in the final stage of the rotor circuit as by so doing, and using a delta connection, the current in each pole of the contactor is reduced to 0.577 times that with

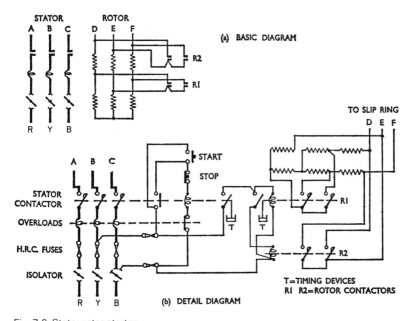

Fig. 7.6. Stator-rotor starter

a two-pole contactor. This may allow a smaller contactor to be used. Fig. 7.7 illustrates the difference in the currents with two-pole and three-pole contactors.

Some degree of speed control can be obtained with the stator-rotor starter by providing for one or more sections of resistance to be left in or out of circuit as required. It is, however, a complicated scheme and, in

$$IC = I \times \frac{1}{1.73} = 0.577I$$

Fig. 7.7. Comparison of currents in poles of rotor contactors. The current carried by a triple-pole contactor is about half that carried by a double-pole contactor

general, if speed control is required on a slip-ring motor, it is better to use a liquid resistance in the rotor circuit, in which case rotor contactors are not required. The liquid resistor can be hand or motor operated and will give an infinitely variable degree of speed control.

Fig. 7.8 shows the application of a liquid resistor to the control of a colliery winder with an induction motor drive. The slip-rings of the motor A are connected to the liquid controller B, and there is a stator reversing switch C for reversing the direction of the stator magnetic field and therefore of rotation. The main switch D is opened automatically to cut off the power in any of several contingencies.

A no-volt release opens the switch if the supply fails but it cannot close itself when the supply is restored. In the event of an overspeed the centrifugal governor F opens the circuit shown by the dotted lines, thus cutting off the supply from the electromagnet which normally holds in the 'on' position the switch of the brake magnet G. The opening of this dotted circuit thus opens the switch controlling the brake magnet so that the emergency brakes are applied. At the same time the main switch is opened by an electrical interlock. A limit switch in the circuit stops the motor in the event of an overwind.

Induction motor reversing

The direction of rotation of three-phase motors is reversed by interchanging two stator leads by means of a pair of contactors. Reversal of direct-on-line started motors is effected by simple change-over switching, but current-limiting starters must be designed to switch off the motor first and then re-start it with the stator leads reversed.

Fig. 7.9 shows a direct-on-line reversing starter. It is similar to the scheme shown in Fig. 7.1 but has two line contactors instead of one, interconnected to provide for reversal of the motor. The two contactors are interlocked to ensure that both cannot be closed at the same time.

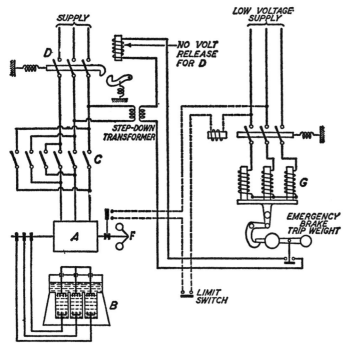

Fig. 7.8. Winder control circuits including liquid-type resistance controller in the rotor circuit of the induction motor

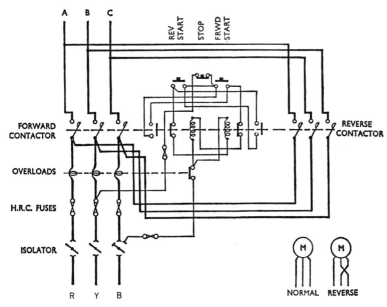

Fig. 7.9. Direct-on-line contactor-type reversing starter

Control circuits

Most control circuits can be regarded as a variation on the simple local control of a direct-on-line starter. This circuit shown in Fig. 7.1 is also shown in a different form in Fig. 7.10(*a*). From this it will be seen that the contactor operating coil is connected across two lines (or one line and neutral) of a supply source, the coil being in series with start and stop pushbuttons, an overload trip switch and an electrical interlock contact on the main isolator. The complete circuit is protected by two h.r.c. fuses. The interlock contact is not always necessary, particularly if an on-load type of isolator is used. The supply source represented by the vertical lines L2 and L3 may be derived from the main circuit, or it may be at some lower voltage from a control circuit transformer.

Fig. 7.10 shows how a number of control circuits for varying methods of control are built up on the basic form. It shows, for example, how for remote control the series circuit between L2 and L3 includes connections to remote pushbutton stations or to pilot switches actuated by changes in temperature, pressure, liquid level, etc. The diagrams also show how in star-delta and stator-rotor control circuits, the additional contactors involved in these forms of starting are connected in parallel with the main (line) contactor through time-delayed auxiliary contacts. In Fig. 7.10(*m*) and (*n*) are shown the connections for controlling reversing and two-speed motors respectively.

It should be noted that contact 7 where it appears is a retaining contact operated by the main contactor, closing when the contactor closes. The contact is in parallel with the start button contacts, its purpose being to retain the circuit after the operator has released the start button which is spring loaded to open on release. In certain circuits the overload trip switch is a latch-out type, i.e. when it opens on overload it is latched out automatically in the open position and must be reset by hand. This precaution is essential in any control scheme of the two-wire type when control is by a simple on/off switch or by some form of pilot switch. In such cases, if the overload switch were self-resetting the contactor would open and close repeatedly. A latch-out switch can be a useful feature on a three-wire control circuit as a safeguard against the operator keeping the start button depressed when there is a persistent overload.

Sequence control schemes

When in plants concerned with continuous processing or handling the motors in various groups must be started in a predetermined sequence, this is arranged by electrical interlocking so that one contactor must be closed before the next one in the sequence can be closed. The majority of such sequence interlocking schemes are series schemes but in some cases parallel interlocking may be necessary.

Fig. 7.11 shows a simple interlocking scheme for three motor drives. The sequence interlocking is arranged so that contactor B cannot be closed until contactor A has closed, and contactor C cannot be closed before B. Thus the starting sequence is A–B–C and is opposite to the flow of material.

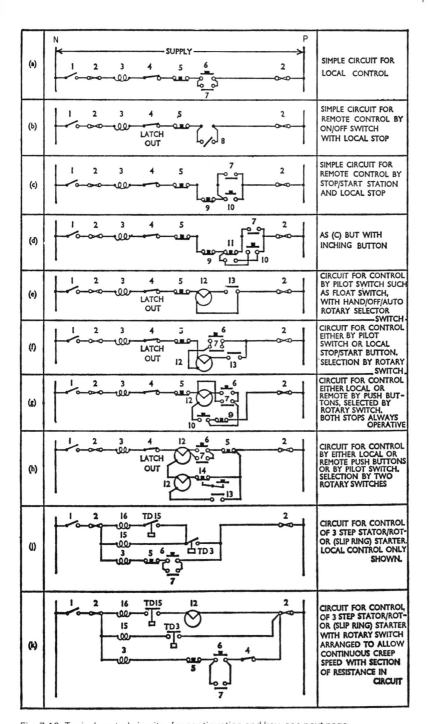

Fig. 7.10. Typical control circuits; for continuation and key, see next page

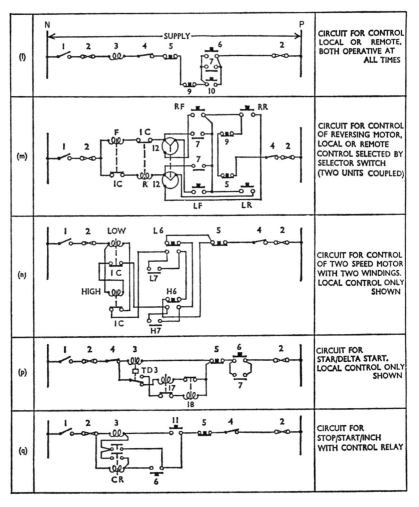

1. Aux. contact on isolator
2. Control circuit fuses
3. Main contactor coil
4. Overload trip switch
5. Local 'stop' button
6. Local 'start' button
7. Retaining contact
8. On/off rotary switch
9. Remote 'stop' button
10. Remote 'start' button
11. Inching 'start' button
12. Rotary selector switch
13. Remote pilot switch e.g. float, pressure or thermostat
14. Remote lock-out 'start/stop'
15. Rotor contactor No. 1
16. Rotor contactor No. 2
17. 'Star' contactor
18. 'Delta' contactor

TD3	Time delay on 3
TD15	Time delay on 15
F	Forward contactor
R	Reverse contactor
LF	Local forward 'start'
LR	Local reverse 'start'
RF	Remote forward 'start'
RR	Remote reverse 'start'
L	Low-speed contactor
H	High-speed contactor
L6	Low-speed 'start' (double contacts)
L7	Low-speed retaining contact
H6	High-speed 'start' (double contacts)
H7	High-speed retaining contact
IC	Interlock contacts on F or R and High or Low
Low:	Low-speed contactor
High:	High-speed contactor
P } N }	Supply across lines or buswires
CR	Control relay

Fig. 7.10 (continued).

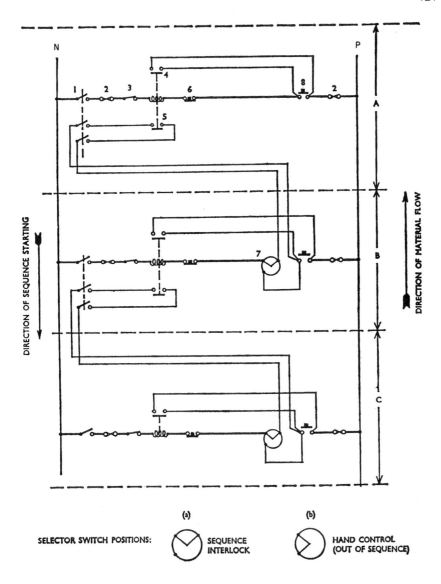

SELECTOR SWITCH POSITIONS:

(a) SEQUENCE INTERLOCK

(b) HAND CONTROL (OUT OF SEQUENCE)

1. Aux. contacts on isolator (normally open)
2. Control circuit fuses
3. Overload trip switch
4. Retaining contact on contactor (normally open)
5. Interlock contact on contactor (normally open)
6. 'Stop' push button
7. Rotary selector switch
8. 'Start' push button
P and N: Supply across two lines or from buswires

Fig. 7.11. Interlocking scheme for sequence starting of three motors

If it is assumed that the three motors are driving conveyors, the scheme ensures that conveyor B must be running before conveyor C can feed material to it; and similarly conveyor A must be running before B can feed it with material. If conveyor B stops, then from the diagram it will be seen that conveyor C also stops and cannot feed material to the stationary conveyor B so that there is no risk of a build-up. At the same time conveyor A can continue to run and discharge whatever material it is carrying.

As the diagram shows, the scheme depends on the use of interconnected auxiliary contacts and it should be noted that those on the isolating switch are duplicated. This is a safety precaution to ensure that when a circuit is isolated, there is no danger of a feed back via interconnected wiring making some point in the unit alive when it appears to be completely isolated and available for a man to work on.

Interlocking schemes are usually provided with some means of enabling tests or inspection on one circuit to be carried out without the need to have the other circuits operating. In Fig. 7.11 rotary switch 7 is provided for this purpose and it has two positions to give 'in sequence' or 'out of sequence'.

In other circumstances it may be necessary in certain operations to feed material direct from conveyor C to conveyor A, missing B. A modification of the rotary switch, or an additional by-pass switch, can be wired into the control circuit to provide this facility.

The scheme in Fig. 7.11 requires that each contactor be closed in turn by an operator pressing the start buttons in the order A–B–C. To indicate that each contactor has actually closed, a red light is usually provided on each circuit.

In an alternative scheme automatic sequence interlocking ensures that after closing contactor A, all succeeding contactors will close automatically. This type of scheme is shown in Fig. 7.12. Contactor A is first closed by the operator using either the local or remote start button. Attached to this contactor is a time delayed auxiliary contact 5. After the time delay, the contact closes to complete the control circuit for contactor B which initiates the closing of contact C in the same way, and so on to the end of the sequence.

Contactor A in Fig. 7.12 can be operated either by local or remote control but B, C and D only have local controls. Rotary switches are provided in each circuit, that in A to select either local or remote control and those in B, C and D to select between 'in sequence' or 'out of sequence'. If the B, C and D rotary switches are set at 'out of sequence', all four motor starters can be operated individually and in any order.

Another example of a simple sequence scheme is shown in Fig. 7.13. It is used with commercial refrigeration plant using a fan and a pump, both driven by squirrel-cage motors with direct-on-line starters, and a compressor driven by a slip-ring motor with a stator-rotor starter. In the scheme for this plant automatic control is provided by a remote thermostat 15 and a pressure cut-out 14. Operation of the plant requires that both the fan and the pump must be running before the compressor can be started. The contactor 5 controlling the fan must therefore close before contactor 6 controlling the pump, and only when 6 is closed can the contactor 7 be closed to start the compressor.

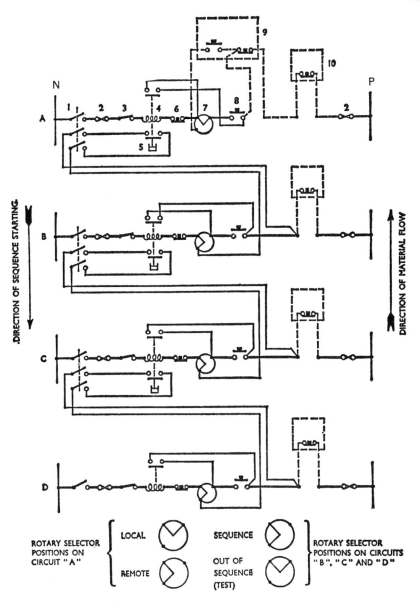

Fig. 7.12. Scheme for automatic sequence interlocking

1. Aux. contacts on isolator (normally open)
2. Control circuit fuses
3. Overload trip switch (normally closed)
4. Retaining contact on contactor (normally open)
5. Time delayed contact on contactor (normally open)
6. 'Stop' button
7. Rotary selector switch
8. 'Start' button
9. Remote 'start/stop' station
10. Remote emergency 'stop' station
P and N – Supply across two lines or from buswires

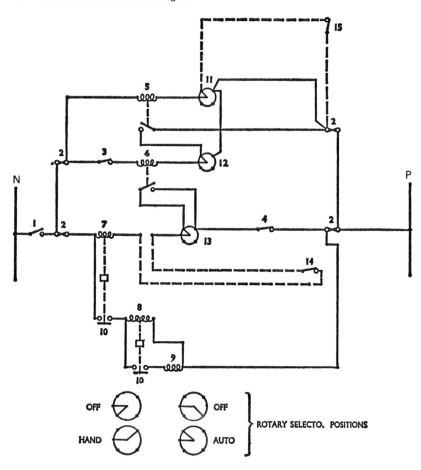

1. Aux. contacts on isolator (normally open)
2. Control circuit fuses
3. Pump motor overload trip switch (normally closed)
4. Compressor motor overload trip switch (normally closed)
5. Fan motor contactor coil
6. Pump motor contactor coil
7. Compressor motor contactor coil (stator)
8. Compressor motor rotor contactor coil (No. 1)
9. Compressor motor rotor contactor coil (No. 2)
10. Delayed closing aux contacts on 7 and 8
11. Rotary switch in fan circuit
12. Rotary switch in pump circuit
13. Rotary switch in compressor circuit
14. High pressure cut-out
15. Thermostat
P and N – Supply across two lines or from buswires

Fig. 7.13. Sequence control of small commercial refrigeration plant. The control ensures that the fan and pump motors are running before the compressor motor is started

When running on automatic control (with all rotary switches set at 'auto') operation of the high pressure cutout to open its contact 14 shuts down the compressor, leaving both the fan and pump running. When the pressure falls, contact 14 recloses and the compressor restarts. Operation of the thermostat to open its contact 15 will shut down the complete plant until a temperature change permits contact 15 to reclose and restart the plant in the proper sequence. The rotary switch enables the plant to be started manually if required.

Although with schemes more complicated than those described the interlocking will be more involved, they will be generally similar in principle. Some schemes require that a complete group of motors must be started in sequence before another group. In this case two separate control boards must be interlocked.

Automatic reclosing circuits

As a contactor is held in by an electrically energized coil, under-voltage protection is inherent. Most modern contactors are designed to hold-in with temporary falls in voltage, in some cases up to about 50 per cent. With a latched-in type of contactor, or a circuit-breaker, a separate no-volt or under-voltage trip is necessary to unlatch the mechanism. To provide for transient voltages the coil may be time-delayed.

In some industrial plants a system disturbance, such as a short-circuit or even the direct-on-line starting of a large motor, may cause the voltage to fall considerably for a matter of seconds so that the control gear operates to disconnect all the motors affected. To avoid having operators going round re-starting the motors the control gear includes an automatic reclosure feature which operates if the voltage recovers withing a prescribed time period.

An automatic reclosure scheme is shown in Fig. 7.14. When the start button is closed, relay R is energized from the bridge rectifier and closes its contacts R1 and R2. Contact R1 completes the circuit to the contactor coil C while contact R2 closes a circuit to charge the capacitor. On a loss of voltage, the contactor will drop out but the relay R will be held closed by the discharge from the capacitor for a period of time determined by the resistance–capacitance values of the time-delay circuit. If the supply voltage recovers before the capacitor has discharged, the contactor will reclose automatically.

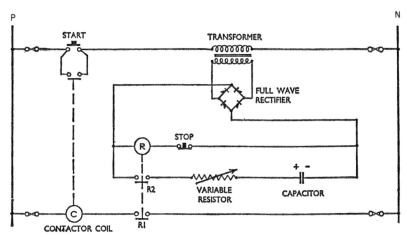

Fig. 7.14. Automatic reclosure scheme

Intrinsically-safe control circuits

In some industrial locations there is a requirement for control circuits at some voltage lower than phase voltage. In mining practice, intrinsically safe remote control circuits operate at, say, 7.5 V but in other installations 110 V a.c. control circuits may be used. This supply may be obtained either by a small voltage transformer in each control gear unit of individual motors or by a larger transformer incorporated in a multi-motor group control board (see page 37).

Remote control circuits which are designed to be intrinsically safe are used extensively below ground in coal mining and to some extent in the petroleum industry. The principle of intrinsic safety is applied in either apparatus or circuits in which the output or consumption of energy is small, and in which means exist to control the energy liberated in sparks when a circuit is interrupted or short-circuited.

The object is to enable electrical equipment to be designed and constructed so that there is no risk of igniting any gas that may be present. In some cases the use of intrinsically-safe circuits may be an alternative to flame-proof gear while in others it may be the only safeguard available. The essential requirement for such a circuit is that any sparking that may occur therein in normal working and with the prescribed components is incapable of causing an explosion of a prescribed flammable gas or vapour.

Control of three-phase commutator motors

For a variety of variable-speed drives the Schrage type of three-phase a.c. commutator motor has several advantages. It can be started direct-on-line, with a low starting current, and has a shunt characteristic. The speed is infinitely variable over a wide speed range above and below synchronous speed without a separate regulator. Acceleration is smooth and the motor develops constant torque throughout the speed range. Efficiency is high at reduced speed and regenerative braking can be applied.

A typical Schrage motor is the type CH produced by GEC Machines in ratings ranging from 1 to 300 h.p. (0.75 to 224 kW) and for frequencies not exceeding 60 Hz and voltages not exceeding 600 V three-phase. The speed of the motor is adjusted by movement of the commutator brushgear, and various schemes developed for the remote control of the type CH motor use either a mechanical or an electrical connection to rotate the brushgear operating spindle.

For local control the motor has a handwheel and for remote mechanical control this is replaced by a chain sprocket coupled to a chain sprocket on a remote handwheel by two lengths of roller chain joined by wire rope tensioned by turnbuckles. For control of the smaller sizes of motor Bowden cable drives can be used.

To control the speed from any distance, the movement of the brushgear operating spindle can be effected by a small pilot motor. Fig. 7.15(a) shows a typical arrangement with pushbutton control. Limit switches are provided to prevent over-travel of the brushgear with control arrangements to return the brushgear to the low-speed position for restarting after a shut-down.

The interlock shown in Fig. 7.15 is a switch connected in the main contactor operating-coil circuit and so fitted that it closes only when the Schrage motor brushgear is set at the low-speed position. For small machines the pilot motor may be a single-phase reversible capacitor motor, controlled by two push-buttons. A larger Schrage motor with a three-phase pilot motor will require reversing contactors, suitably interlocked, for the pilot motor as shown in Fig. 7.15(b). From this diagram, it can be seen that when the main motor is switched off, the pilot motor automatically runs back to return the brushgear to the low-speed position ready for the next direct-on-line start. When the stop button is operated, the main contactor and the auxiliary switches (1) revert to their respective normal positions,

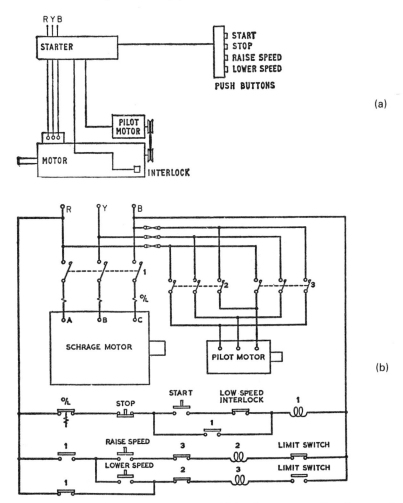

Fig. 7.15. Schrage-type commutator motor with brushgear operated by pilot motor for controlling speed. (a) Typical arrangement with pushbutton control for starting and stopping, and raising and lowering speed. (b) Circuit for Schrage motor started direct-on-line and with brushgear position-controlled three-phase pilot motor

some being 'normally-on', as illustrated in Fig. 7.15(*b*). If the low-speed interlock is open at this time, the low-speed limit switch will be in the closed position, consequently a circuit will be complete through the 'lower speed' contactor-operating coil (3), which becomes energized. The 'lower speed' contactor 3 will then close and the pilot motor will run to the starting position of the brushgear, at which point the low-limit switch opens and the low-speed interlock closes.

Pre-set control

Many applications of variable speed motors require that the machines run up to a pre-determined speed automatically. This can be accomplished either by rheostatic starting or by the use of a pre-set speed controller.

Rheostat starting

When rheostat starting is adopted, the ends of each secondary phase of the type CH motor are brought out to terminals and connected to starting resistors. A value of starting resistance is specified that ensures adequate starting torque with the brushgear in the low-speed position and also limits the starting current to a low value with the brushgear in the high-speed position. Because of the necessity of meeting these two contradictory requirements, this method of starting is only permissible if the speed range is short. No interlock is necessary on the motor brushgear, but there is the usual interlocking in the starter to ensure that the resistance is all-in before the line contactor closes. Although the method of starting is similar to that of a slip-ring induction motor, a standard starter is not usually suitable as the secondary phases of the type CH motor must be separately connected. Fig. 7.16 shows diagrammatically a machine with a hand-operated brushgear and rheostatic starting.

Although normally used only with hand-operated brushgear for which rheostatic starting is the only method of starting at a pre-set speed, rheostatic starting can be used with a pilot motor. It has the advantage that after a momentary shutdown there is no time wasted while the brushgear runs back to the low-speed position; it is not normally recommended unless this feature is of outstanding importance.

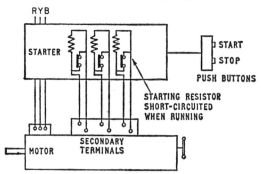

Fig. 7.16. Hand-operated brushgear with rheostatic starting

Pre-set speed controller type C719

For type CH 4800 and 5600 motors, the standard arrangement of electrical operating gear incorporating a three-phase pilot motor has the limit switches and interlock mounted in a switch unit on the operating gear base. The switch unit includes a pre-set device using cam-operated switches. This is designated the type C719-A preset speed controller. The speed-setting knob is concentric with the operating sprocket and adjustment is normally made with the motor at rest. A small dial and pointer is mounted behind the knob. The hinged door which gives access to the knob is secured by a shrouded screw for which a special spanner is provided. Fig. 7.17 illustrates the arrangement. Since adjustment is normally made with the machine at

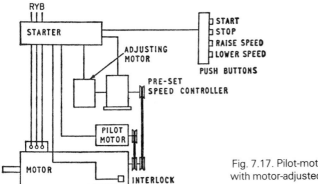

Fig. 7.17. Pilot-motor-operated brushgear with motor-adjusted speed controller

rest pushbuttons are usually provided and are connected so that any speed may be selected up to the pre-set speed. If desired, the pushbuttons can be connected in such a way as to permit the controller setting to be overridden by them.

The arrangement of the C719-A pre-set controller is shown diagrammatically in Fig. 7.18(a) and the method of connection in a typical control circuit in Fig. 7.18(b).

The C719-B pre-set speed controller is interchangeable in fixing dimensions with C719-A, but a separate speed-setting spindle protrudes at the back; this can be coupled to an operating motor or remotely controlled by mechanical means. Continuous, and if necessary automatic, speed adjustment is therefore possible. Fig. 7.19 shows this type adjusted by a single-phase geared motor unit. A similar arrangement is possible with provision for automatic adjustment or adjustment from user's remote handwheel. The equipment is supplied with a bare spindle at the back of the controller for coupling to the setting device, which should be provided with enough friction to prevent creeping of the setting spindle during speed changes.

The type C748 pre-set controller can be used in conjunction with floating or compensating rolls to maintain constant tension in paper, cloth and textile yarns. In such cases the controller is fitted with chain sprockets on both shafts, one driven by the floating roll mechanism and the other coupled to the brushgear operating spindle. Two or more mechanically

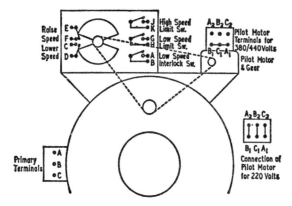

a. Motor terminals.

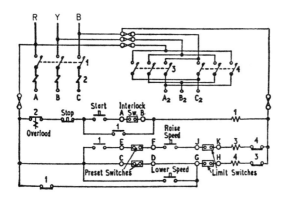

b. Typical control diagram.

Fig. 7.18. Connections of a.c. commutator motor with type C719–A preset speed controller

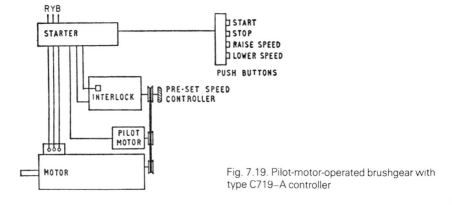

Fig. 7.19. Pilot-motor-operated brushgear with type C719–A controller

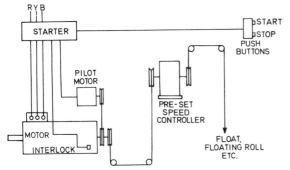

Fig. 7.20. Pilot-motor-operated brushgear with type C748 preset speed controller automatically adjusted

independent drives can thus be kept in synchronism by the action of the floating roll, with very light tension in the material supporting the roll as the torque required to operate the controller is very light. In a similar way the speed of a pump can be controlled by the position of a float coupled to the controller. Fig 7.20 shows diagrammatically an arrangement of an automatically adjusted pre-set speed controller.

Closed loop control

For a given speed setting, the inherent shunt characteristic of a Schrage motor will give a decrease of speed from no-load to full-load between 5 and 10 per cent of the maximum speed of the motor. This variation depends to some extent on the size of the motor and the speed for which the brushgear is set.

Although this method is normally acceptable, certain applications (e.g. in the paper and printing industries) demand a control of speed which can be obtained by using a closed-loop control scheme. By this method the speed can be regulated to within ±1 per cent of maximum speed at any desired speed, independent of changing loads or supplies.

Change-pole three-phase induction motors

On a given supply frequency, the synchronous speed of an induction motor is determined by the number of pairs of its stator poles. On 50 Hz, a four-pole motor, for example, has a synchronous speed of $50/2 = 25$ revolutions per second, or $25 \times 60 = 1500$ rev/min. The principle of changing the number of poles and thereby changing the speed is adopted for drives requiring a choice of two, three or four fixed speeds.

Two different numbers of stator poles from a single stator winding can be produced by tapping the stator winding in six positions and connecting the tappings by external switching. If the switching is arranged so that the direction of current flow is reversed in alternate pole groups of coils, twice as many poles are produced and the motor operates at half speed. This consequent-pole method of pole changing gives 2:1 speed ratio. The tapped stator winding may be wound for 2 and 4, 4 and 8, or 6 and 12 poles, and so on, to obtain the corresponding speeds.

Fig. 7.21 illustrates typical winding and switching arrangements for a two-speed consequent-pole winding to develop either constant power or constant torque. A drum type controller may be employed for making the necessary changes of connections or, alternatively, contactors may be used under the control of external pushbuttons and suitably interlocked to ensure that only the correct contactors are closed together.

Change-pole motors are usually of the squirrel-cage type since it is then only necessary to switch the stator windings. With slip-ring motors it may be necessary to have alternative rotor windings and additional slip rings to permit reconnection of the rotor windings.

Obtaining two fixed speeds at ratios other than 2:1 was, until recently, invariably accomplished by superimposing two completely separate stator windings in the stator slots. Although other single winding arrangements were available these required a large number of terminals and the necessary control gear was too complex and expensive for normal use.

Fig. 7.22 illustrates typical winding and switching arrangements for two-speed motors with double winding. A separate winding for each speed is used when it is necessary for each speed to maintain control over the driven machine when changing speed. The separate windings allow the second winding to be connected to the supply before the first is disconnected.

As mentioned below, there is now a single-winding alternative to the use of double-wound stator windings for other than 2:1 speed ratios, i.e. the pole-amplitude modulated winding.

When a three-phase induction motor is required to operate at three or four different speeds, a double-wound motor can have either or both of the superimposed windings of the change-pole type.

Since the introduction of the pole-amplitude modulated (PAM) induction motor winding, two fixed speeds have become available from a single tapped winding at ratios other than 2:1. As in the 2:1 tapped winding, six terminals only are required, and to give pole changing one part of the winding is reversed with respect to another, but in the PAM winding coil reversal is not symmetrically arranged.

Electronic speed control

The a.c. induction motor is essentially a fixed-speed machine, but due to its inherent sturdiness and simplicity various ingenious means, as previously described, have been adopted for speed control.

With increasing reliability in solid-state devices, the modern move is towards electronic methods of obtaining smooth and easy speed variation, generally from the basic equation that rotor speed is proportional to frequency. Here frequency changes are obtained by static inverters based on the use of thyristors. Speed variation by voltage control is also adopted.

We can summarize by stating that the development of the thyristor in the 1960s revolutionized variable-speed motor methods because of its small size, simplicity and versatility. Initially the thyristor was employed to control the speed of d.c. motors, but now it has become a commercial proposition for the speed control of a.c. machines. In the Renold

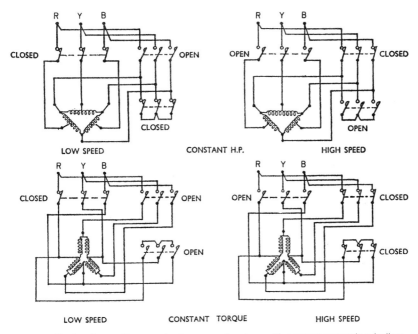

Fig. 7.21. Basic primary diagrams for two-speed motors with consequent-pole winding giving a speed ratio of 2:1

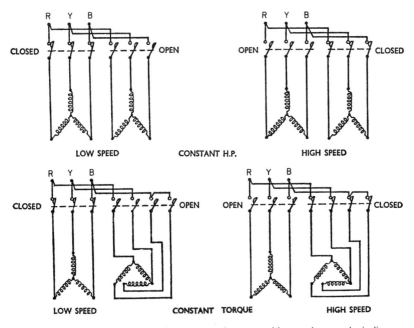

Fig. 7.22. Basic primary diagrams for two-speed motors with superimposed windings

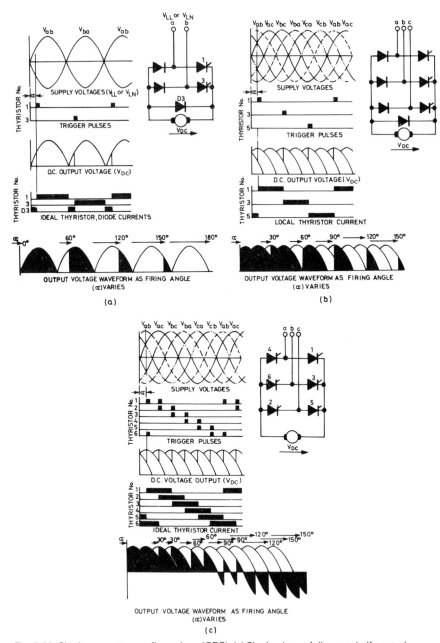

Fig. 7.23. Single converter configurations (GEC). (a) Single-phase, full-wave, half control. (b) Three-phase, full-wave, half control; single-ended, non-inverting or three-pulse. (c) Three-phase, fully controlled; or single-ended, inverting; or six-pulse.

Types (a) and (b) drive in one direction only and are incapable of regenerative braking. Type (c) drives in one direction only and provides regenerative braking if the load attempts to drive the motor in the reverse direction

variable-speed controller the starter embodies electronic circuitry which changes the fixed-frequency (50 Hz) a.c. supply into a variable-frequency three-phase supply enabling induction motors to run at a variable speed.

With an a.c. supply applied, the thyristor gate can be triggered at any point in the positive half-cycle, enabling the amplitude of the output direct voltage to be controlled between a maximum and zero. Thyristors can be connected in various GEC motor configurations (Fig. 7.23) and can be arranged to rectify (a.c. to d.c.) or to invert (d.c. to a.c.).

The GEC method of thyristor-controlled a.c. drive operation is obtained by varying the voltage and frequency applied to a cage induction motor or to a synchronous motor, or by absorbing power from the slip rings of the slip-ring induction motor. Variation of the frequency may be achieved in various ways, illustrated in Fig. 7.24.

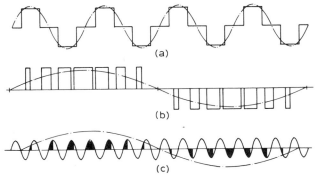

(a)

(b)

(c)

Fig. 7.24. Variations in frequency supply. Each method can be fed to different types of a.c. motor, resulting in a range of characteristics. (a) Quasi square wave: creates a crude sine wave with square pulses, then varies the frequency. (b) Pulse width modulation: simulates different frequencies by modulating the width of pulses. (c) Cyclo converter: chops the supply voltage waveform to give a lower frequency

A practical Danfloss circuit (Fig. 7.25) contains three static inverters. Here it is found necessary to convert the fundamental sine wave to quasi-square.

The quasi-square wave system makes for a design which is electrically rugged and is suitable for starting and for stopping of parallel-connected motors without damage to the inverter, in addition to enabling a high starting torque to be produced.

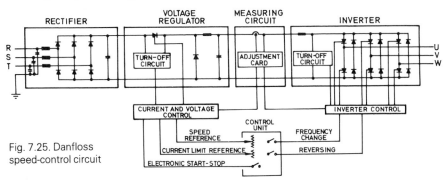

Fig. 7.25. Danfloss speed-control circuit

8 D.C. motor control

Although d.c. distribution to consumers has been practically superseded by the standard a.c. systems in the United Kingdom, and is becoming obsolete elsewhere, there is a steady increase in the use of d.c. motors for drives for which they are superior to any a.c. motor. Their speed/torque characteristics are an advantage for many drives and with suitable control gear the speed can be varied infinitely over a wide range. Large d.c. motors can be reversed rapidly against high inertia loads and braked by regenerative schemes that return power to the supply system. Efficiency is high over a wide speed range and there are no problems resulting from poor power factor, as with induction motors.

To realize the advantages of the d.c. motor with only a standard a.c. supply available it is necessary for the user to install converting or rectifying plant. One well-known method of providing a d.c. variable-speed motor drive is to use a Ward Leonard set. In addition there are the developed static rectifier type of control units used for an individual motor that can be completely and precisely controlled by manual and/or automatic adjustments. These units are particularly effective for a variety of industrial drives requiring an accuracy of control and a speed range that cannot be obtained with any type of a.c. motor.

Only the smallest d.c. motors can be started by direct connection to the mains. To achieve the essential limitation of the starting current through the armature, it is necessary to introduce a series resistor or start the motor by regulating the applied voltage from zero up to the normal value.

A device for cutting out the series resistance in steps, the faceplate starter (Fig. 8.1), is used only for the infrequent starting of motors up to about 11 kW. For many applications the starter is of the type using contactors to cut out the series resistance in steps. Drum type starters (Fig. 8.2) are also used, especially when a large number of small steps is required to minimize the current peaks during acceleration.

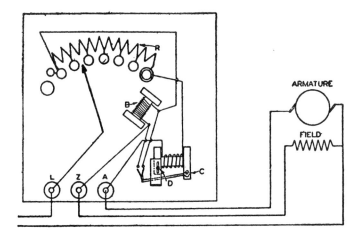

Fig. 8.1. Faceplate starter with no-volt release (B) and overload release (C). Used with a shunt-wound motor, the no-volt release is connected in series with the shunt field and is short-circuited when the overload release operates

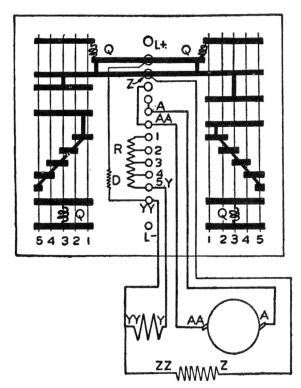

Fig. 8.2. Drum-type reversing controller for a compound wound motor. Movement of the rotating contact assembly cuts out the steps of the resistor and makes the connections for rotation of the motor in either direction when the control handle is moved clockwise or anti-clockwise

Time-element starter

In the time-element starter, the cutting out of successive sections of resistance is governed by time-delay devices. The circuits of this type of starter with two sections of resistance are shown in Fig. 8.3. With this scheme, operation of the start pushbutton closes the main contactor C to connect the motor to the line in series with the starting resistor. At the same time the auxiliary contacts C_1, carried by the main contactor, also close to energize the coil of the timing relay TR and bridge the start pushbutton contacts. When the pushbutton is released, the main contactor and timing relay coils are energized through the contacts C_1.

After a time interval, determined by the setting of TR, contact 1 of this relay closes to energize the coil of accelerating contactor 2R so that the contactor closes to cut out the first section of the resistor. After a further interval contact 2 closes to energize the coil of contactor 3R to cut out the second section of resistance and the motor runs up to full speed.

In schemes where several accelerating contactors are used, the coil circuits of all except the last one may be fed through an auxiliary contact on the last contactor. This contact opens when the last contactor closes, and disconnects the intermediate accelerating contactors.

It will be noted in Fig. 8.3 that the coil circuits are fed through the overload relay contacts OL and the stop pushbutton contacts in series, so that the opening of either causes all the contactors to open. Restarting can be effected only by pressing the start pushbutton provided that the stop pushbutton has been released and that the overload relay contacts are reclosed. With large starters, closing of the accelerating contactors may be controlled by contacts operated in sequence by a small motor.

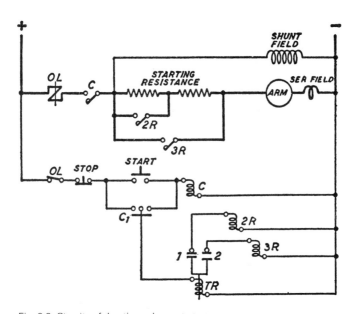

Fig. 8.3. Circuits of d.c. time-element starter

Current-element starter

Starters of the automatic current-element type are used for motors driving variable loads where the starting conditions also vary and the rate of acceleration with heavy loads is lower than that with light loads. The requirements of the starting duty are met by arranging that the starting resistor sections are cut out only when the respective current peaks have fallen to a predetermined value. One of the simplest ways of providing this form of control is by the use of series relays to control the closing of the accelerating contactors.

A typical scheme is shown in Fig. 8.4. There are three sections of starting resistance and three series relays. The contacts of these relays remain closed when the current in the coil is below a predetermined value.

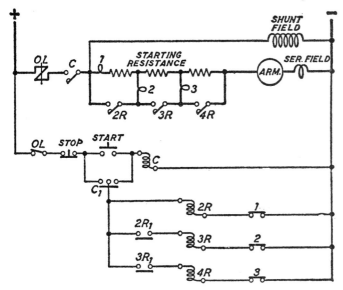

Fig. 8.4. Circuits of d.c. current-element starter

Pressure on the start pushbutton closes the main contactor C and its auxiliary contacts C_1 to establish a circuit for the operating coil as well as the accelerating contactors (as in Fig. 8.3). The initial starting current which flows as soon as the main contactor closes, energizes series relay 1 which accordingly opens its contacts.

The action of the relay is rapid enough to prevent the first accelerating contactor 2R closing with the closing of contacts C_1. These contacts may also be arranged to close as late as possible after the closing of the main contacts C, so providing a further safeguard. As the motor accelerates the current falls and, at a predetermined value, depending on the setting of relay 1, the armature of this relay releases, thus closing its contacts and energizing contactor 2R. With this closed, the motor current corresponding to the second switching peak now flows through the coil of relay 2 and causes its contacts to open before the second accelerating contactor R can be closed by the action of the auxiliary contacts $2R_1$ on contactor 2R.

As the motor continues to accelerate, the current in the coil of relay 2 decreases to a value where the relay releases, thus completing the coil circuit of the second accelerating contactor 3R. A similar sequence occurs with relay 3 and contactor 4R, thus completing the starting operation. It should be noted that the coil resistance of relays 2 and 3 is negligible compared with that of the starting resistor sections so that with the closing of contactors 2R and 3R the current through the relay coils is virtually the total current of the motor.

Counter-e.m.f. starter

With the counter-e.m.f. d.c. motor starter, the time taken to cut out the starting resistor is determined by the time taken for the counter e.m.f. of the motor to rise to a particular value from the moment of switching on. The starting time depends on the load, as with current-element starters.

Referring to Fig. 8.5, the scheme includes one resistor and the operating coil of the accelerating contactor is connected directly across the motor armature. Initially therefore, the voltage across the coil is zero. When

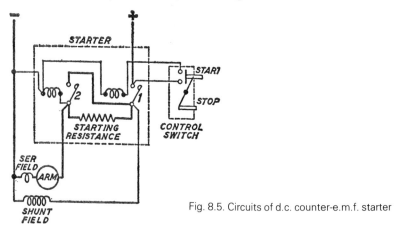

Fig. 8.5. Circuits of d.c. counter-e.m.f. starter

contactor 1 closes to connect the motor to the supply in series with the resistor, the motor accelerates and the counter e.m.f. rises in proportion to its speed until the voltage on the coil of contactor 2 is sufficient to close the contactor.

The point of closing is adjustable and the setting is usually such to close the contactor at about 60 per cent of the full line voltage. When the motor is switched off the contactor is held closed until the voltage has dropped to about one-third of line voltage, and it will not release until the motor speed has decreased to a corresponding low value. If the start pushbutton is operated before the speed has dropped enough for contactor 2 to release, the motor will then be connected directly to the line. If this is not permissible, the contactor 2 operating coil is fed through auxiliary contacts on contactor 1 which open when the contactor opens.

Although this method of starting usually employs only one step of starting resistance, the scheme can include several accelerating contactors operating at different voltage settings so that they close in the correct sequence and at the proper intervals. With this scheme it may be necessary to switch out intermediate contactors by means of auxiliary contacts on subsequent contactors in order to prevent over-heating of the low voltage coils that must be used.

Reversing schemes

The direction of rotation of a d.c. motor may be changed by reversing either the armature or the field connections, but not both as this would result in the motor rotating in the same direction as before.

A manually operated double-pole double-throw switch can be used for armature reversal with some form of electrical or mechanical interlock to prevent switch operation while the motor is running. The circuit must also be arranged so that there is always a discharge path for the shunt field when the motor is switched off.

Fig. 8.6 shows the connections of a pushbutton-operated reversing counter-e.m.f. starter. It has one accelerating contactor and two double-pole reversing contactors F and R with auxiliary contacts F_1, R_1 which close when the contactors close. An interlock is usually provided to prevent F and R closing together. Operation of the forward pushbutton closes contactor F and when the pushbutton is released the circuit is maintained by contacts F_1. Similarly, operation of the reverse pushbutton closes contactor R. The direction of current flow through the armature, and therefore the direction of rotation, is different in each case.

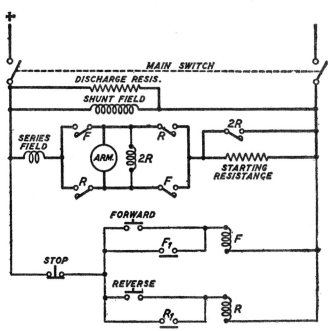

Fig. 8.6. Circuits of reversing d.c. starter with counter-e.m.f. acceleration control

Operation of the stop pushbutton releases whichever of contactors F or R is in operation and thus stops the motor. Contactor 2R does not open until the motor has slowed down to a speed giving a sufficiently low counter-e.m.f., so stopping and reversing before this would have the effect of connecting the motor to the line without starting resistance. The methods of acceleration shown in Figs. 8.3 and 8.4 which may be employed in conjunction with reversing contactors do not have this disadvantage.

Braking methods

Rapid braking of d.c. motors (and a.c. motors of the induction type) may be obtained by plugging, i.e. by changing the connections to those used normally to reverse the motor. Particularly suitable for rapid stopping, the method uses change-over contactors and some device to ensure that when the motor has stopped it does not actually reverse. The device is usually some form of centrifugal switch mounted on the motor shaft.

Dynamic braking is a smooth, powerful and controllable method that can be applied to a d.c. motor by using the connections shown in Fig. 8.7.

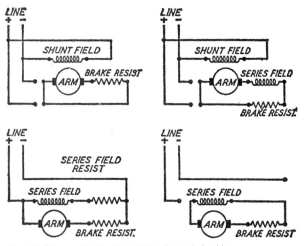

Fig. 8.7. Four methods of applying dynamic braking

The motor armature is disconnected from the supply and reconnected across a resistor. With shunt and compound motors, the shunt field remains connected to the supply, and the armature then functions as that of a generator causing current to flow in the closed circuit including the brake resistor. With series motors, the series field may remain connected to the supply in series with a resistor, or may be included in the closed braking circuit.

As the motor speed falls during dynamic braking, the retarding effect decreases due to the progressive reduction in current and becomes negligible at low speeds. Final stopping may be achieved by a friction brake. The dynamic braking effect can be maintained to a large extent by cutting out the brake resistor in steps to maintain the current.

Speed-control schemes

The scheme used for the speed control of a d.c. motor depends on the requirement for the machine it drives since this determines the type of motor and the range of control necessary.

For speeds below a specified base speed, control can be effected by a resistor in series with the armature, and when low speeds are required, in conjunction with an armature shunt resistor or divertor. Speed control above base speed can be effected by varying the strength of the motor field, e.g. with a shunt motor by including a variable resistor in the field circuit. For the widest ranges of speed control there are schemes for the independent regulation of the voltage applied to the armature.

Fig. 8.8 shows a shunt field regulator with an interlock to prevent the motor being started up with a weak field. The electromagnet M is energized from the supply and holds up the armature P while it remains energized. If the motor is shut down by means of the starter, the armature P is released and connects the two contacts at Q to short-circuit all resistance in the regulator and so ensure full field when the motor is started again. As the starter is operated to the full-on position, M is energized but is not strong enough to lift the armature. It will only hold it after it has been raised by movement of the regulator arm.

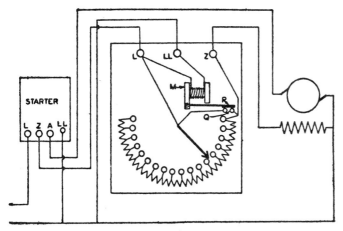

Fig. 8.8. Connections of a shunt field regulator

Used for a variety of industrial drives, the Ward Leonard system provides for control of a d.c. motor by variation of the voltage applied to the armature and independent variation of the shunt field of the motor. The scheme is shown in Fig. 8.9.

In this particular scheme an a.c induction motor drives a d.c. generator which supplies the work motor, and an exciter which supplies the generator and motor shunt fields at constant voltage. The speed of the motor is controlled by adjusting the generator shunt field to vary the voltage applied to the motor armature. Speed ranges of the order of 10:1 can be obtained with the basic scheme but greater ranges can be obtained with

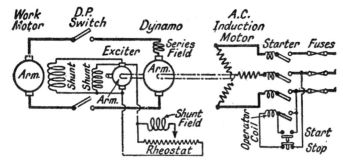

Fig. 8.9. Ward Leonard control of d.c. motor speed

schemes developed specifically for the operation of a particular industrial drive.

When the work motor must be reversible, a reversing type potentio-meter is used and connected as shown in Fig. 8.10. With the moving contacts in position (*a*) the potential at both ends of the field is the same and no current flows through the winding. In position (*b*) full field excitation is obtained in a given direction and at (*c*) the excitation is a maximum in the opposite direction. Between positions (*a*) and (*b*) or (*c*) a range of intermediate values is obtainable between zero and maximum.

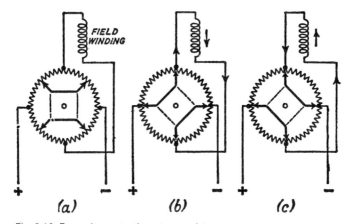

Fig. 8.10. Reversing potentiometer regulator

Controlled-rectifier systems

Various electronic a.c./d.c. rectifiers are used in d.c. motor control schemes to vary speed by regulating the applied voltage. These rectifiers may be grouped in two categories: mercury-arc units and solid-state thyristors.

In the mercury-arc unit category are the ignitron and the mercury-arc convector, which are similar in principle to the thyratron but with a mercury-pool cathode instead of a heated filament. The ignitron is a single-anode unit which, instead of a grid control, has an ignitor electrode that is energized at the instant that the discharge must be started.

The mercury-arc convertor may have one or more anodes and is similar in principle to the mercury-arc rectifiers used at one time only to provide general d.c. supplies. It is designed to work with grid control over a wide load range supplying reversible variable-speed d.c. motors.

The purpose of grid control is to adjust the instant at which during the positive half-cycle of applied voltage the rectifier begins to function. Control is effected by varying the phase angle between the grid and anode potentials. With this phase-shift control, the mean value of the d.c. output voltage can be reduced progressively by increasing the phase angle between the grid and anode potentials; or in other words, by progressively delaying the instant at which the anode is fired.

In the case of rectifiers used for motor control, the control grids are energized from peaking circuits which produce a steep-fronted pulse of voltage. Fig. 8.11 shows two typical peaking circuits and the voltage they generate. A peak of negative polarity occurs 180° after the positive peak, but since the grid can conduct only in one direction the negative peak has no effect on the control characteristics. A negative grid-bias voltage is usually included in the circuit to ensure that the grid is energized only on the steepest part of the front of the pulse.

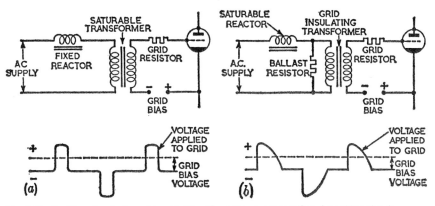

Fig. 8.11. Peaking circuits for grid excitation of a mercury-arc rectifier. A peaking circuit produces a steep-front pulse of voltage, which controls the instant at which the rectifier begins to conduct during every positive half-cycle of applied a.c. voltage

Automatic control systems

Most variable-speed d.c. motor control schemes are used to provide for automatic regulation of some kind of industrial processing operation and are required to maintain a set speed, or adjust speed to maintain a processing condition, in response to a signal indicating a departure from a normal datum. In the simplest case, if the speed of a machine is to be maintained at a constant value, then any tendency to a higher or lower speed would be corrected immediately by a signal initiating the operation of the motor speed controller.

Automatic control schemes intended to give rapid and precise regulation almost invariably include some type of amplifier which is necessary to deal with the weak control signals that are involved when the automatic controller has to be actuated with the minimum deviation between the actual and desired values of the controlled quantity.

In an automatic control scheme, the control signal is, in effect, a feedback of information which enables the power controller to take corrective action as required. Referring to Fig. 8.12, the motor speed is monitored by a tacho-generator generating a voltage V_t which is proportional to speed. This voltage is compared with the reference voltage

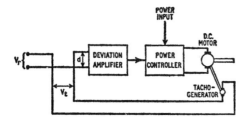

Fig. 8.12. Closed-loop feedback automatic control system

V_r which is proportional to the desired speed, and can be adjusted to alter the value of the desired speed. The difference between V_t and V_r is the deviation d (the error voltage) which is measured and amplified by the deviation amplifier. The signal thus obtained is used to activate the power controller which in this case regulates the input to the motor and therefore its speed.

With some automatic control schemes, the amplifier functions simple to regulate a control circuit. For example, in the basic scheme shown in Fig. 8.13, the amplifier controls the input to the generator shunt field winding of a Ward Leonard set, and therefore the output voltage to the motor.

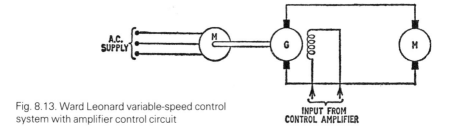

Fig. 8.13. Ward Leonard variable-speed control system with amplifier control circuit

Many of the present-day control schemes use an amplifier to control the output of a static rectifier supplying the d.c. motor, the speed being regulated by varying the output. Fig. 8.14 shows a scheme using a saturable reactor and a semiconductor rectifier. The a.c. input to the rectifier, and therefore the d.c. output, is controlled by the current through the d.c. control winding on the saturable reactor. The control winding is supplied from the control amplifier, and its output is determined at any time by the error voltage.

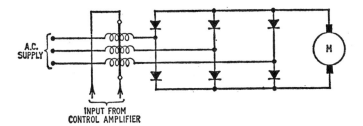

Fig. 8.14. Saturable reactor-rectifier speed-regulating scheme with amplifier control circuit

Other control schemes include static rectifiers with elements such as thyratrons, ignitrons, excitrons, grid-controlled mercury-arc rectifiers or thyristors (silicon controlled rectifiers).

Solid-state control equipment

In recent years the scope of application of the mercury-arc convertor has been extended by the use of new control techniques made possible by the introduction of reliable semiconductor devices. However, the present tendency is towards the increasing use of entirely solid-state d.c. motor control equipments based on silicon diodes and thyristors. Further development of the latter is resulting in solid-state equipment becoming available for d.c. motors of increasingly higher power ratings.

Fig. 8.15 shows the circuits of a thyristor-controlled variable-speed drive unit for constant-torque d.c. motors in the range 6–56 kW. Designed for 400/440 V three-phase 50 Hz supplies, the units have a maximum d.c. output voltage of either 400 V or 460 V and are capable of providing a range of speed control greater than 20:1. Thyristors are incorporated in a simple bridge-connected circuit, the output of which is controlled by an amplifier and firing circuit. A closed-loop system of speed control uses a reference voltage from a speed-setting potentiometer and a reset signal from the armature voltage. Compensation is included for the IR drop in the motor armature. When high speed-setting accuracies are required, a reset signal can be provided by a tachogenerator. The field supply is obtained from a separate rectifier employing a full-wave bridge circuit.

As shown in Fig. 8.15, the motor armature is supplied through a three-phase bridge-connected rectifier via a d.c. contactor. The main rectifier has silicon diodes in one half of the bridge circuit and thyristors in the other. The output of the main rectifier bridge depends upon the point in each cycle at which the thyristors are made to conduct, which is determined by the d.c. voltage level applied to the firing circuit.

The d.c. voltage level is derived from an amplifier, the output of which is proportional to the difference in voltage (error voltage) between that set on the speed-setting potentiometer and the voltage across the armature of the motor. If the potentiometer is rotated to obtain a slight increase in speed, the voltage across the potentiometer rises immediately whereas the reset voltage remains the same. The resultant increase in error voltage is

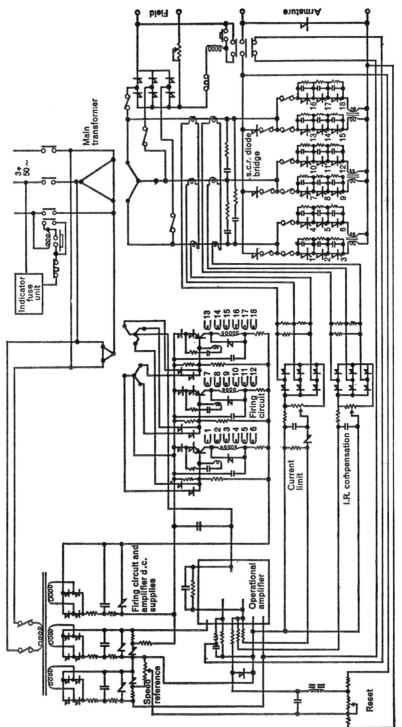

Fig. 8.15. Thyristor-controlled variable-speed drive unit

sufficient to drive the amplifier to full output (under current limit) and thus causes the motor speed to increase. With increasing motor speed, the armature voltage increases until once again the error voltage is reduced virtually to zero.

Since the reset signal is taken from the output voltage applied to the armature, an increase of load on the motor would cause the speed to drop owing to the IR voltage drop in the motor – a factor which prevents the armature voltage/speed relation being linear. To compensate for this voltage drop, a signal proportional to armature current is fed to the amplifier, in series with the armature voltage reset signal, in a direction to compensate for load changes. When a direct-coupled tachogenerator provides the reset signal, its output is used instead of the motor armature voltage.

To prevent the control unit and motor being overloaded when speed changes are being made, a current-limit circuit limits current to a predetermined value. A slow run-in circuit ensures that the armature current builds up slowly when the equipment is first switched on, and before the current-limit circuit has become effective.

Connected across the a.c. side of the rectifier bridge are resistor-capacitor circuits which absorb external and self-generated voltage surges. In series with each diode and thyristor there is a special fuse to clear the circuit in the event of a device failure or a d.c. short-circuit. When any one of these main fuses fails, an indicating fuse in the fuse-trip unit also fails and operates a micro-switch which in turn trips the main contactor.

The output of the bridge is fed to the motor armature via a pushbutton-operated d.c. contactor, the closing coil of which is supplied from the same source as that for the field. In the event of a field supply failure, the armature supply is also disconnected automatically.

Fig. 8.16 shows a d.c. variable-speed drive scheme with features also used in the scheme of Fig. 8.15, but employing a transductor to vary the voltage applied to the motor armature. For controlling d.c. motors of 11–150 kW with constant-torque outputs, the control units are designed for 415 V three-phase 50 Hz supplies, providing a variable output voltage of 0–460 V d.c. for the armature and a 110 V d.c. constant voltage supply for the motor field. The units provide for a range of speed control of up to 40:1, or greater for special applications.

The equipment incorporates an auto-excited three-phase transductor the output from which is rectified in a three-phase silicon diode bridge circuit. The output of the transductor depends on the degree of excitation of the core, which is controlled by the current flowing in the d.c. windings. A two-stage voltage- and power-amplifier feeds the control windings on the transductor and hence controls the output voltage and therefore the motor speed. The input to the amplifier is the difference in voltage between that set by a speed-setting potentiometer and the voltage applied to the motor armature. The scheme includes a current-limit circuit and an IR drop compensating circuit.

Although the units are designed primarily for the control of d.c. motors, they can also be used for applications where a regulated variable-voltage d.c. supply is required.

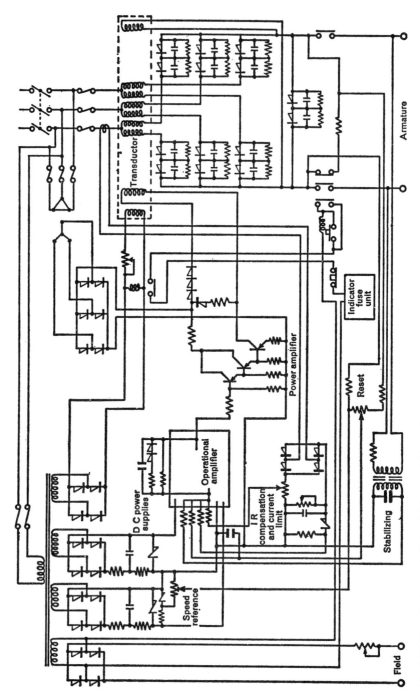

Fig. 8.16. Transductor-controlled variable-speed drive unit

Thyristor control

The Necontrol d.c. motor can be controlled in speed by varying the voltage applied to the armature winding making use of electronic components. Power transistors provide solid-state control of voltage and current with an efficiency of about 98 per cent. The d.c. thyristor-controlled system uses a permanent magnet or conventional shunt-wound field motor, and has the advantage of constant torque throughout the speed range, which in most cases is infinite.

Consider a half-controlled full-wave bridge rectifier as shown in Fig. 8.17, where T_1 and T_2 are thyristors, D_1, D_2 and D_3 are diodes, and M is the d.c. motor. After a delay angle, T_1 is triggered and current flows in the direction of the arrows shown in the figure during the positive cycle. In practice the thyristor is often triggered by one large pulse (approximately 5 V peak) followed by a train of small pulses for the rest of the duration of the sine wave. During the negative cycle, T_2 is fired at a similar delay angle and the resultant wave shape when applied to a d.c. motor is given in Fig. 8.18. By increasing the phase angle, the speed of the d.c. motor will be increased proportionally. The description of the single-phase bridge is used for simplicity; the principle is identical for three-phase and six-phase control.

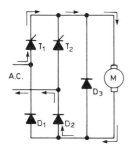

Fig. 8.17. Full-wave half-controlled thyristor bridge

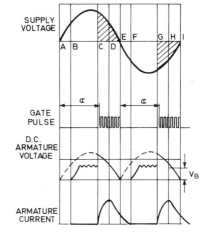

Fig. 8.18. Bridge waveforms

The current loop

Although the speed of a d.c. shunt motor is directly proportional to the armature voltage for constant excitation, losses are always present in a d.c. motor. IR losses, windage and frictional losses vary in accordance with the load and speed. For this reason, it is necessary to have an automatic regulator which controls the phase angle so that the correct armature voltage can be applied to maintain constant speed regardless of load.

The regulator corrects for differences in mains supply and other variations in the motor so that the speed deviation is kept to a minimum.

For example, an increase in the mains supply voltage would cause an increase in the average d.c. output; therefore the phase angle would have to be decreased proportionally so as to reduce the average voltage to the correct value which will give the desired speed.

The Necontrol loop system shown in Fig. 8.19 uses armature voltage for feedback into an operational amplifier which, in this application, amplifies the difference between it and the desired speed obtained from a potentiometer.

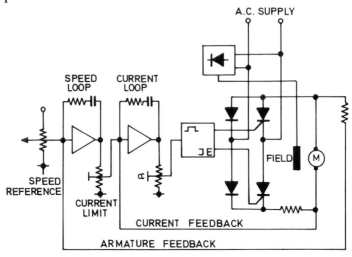

Fig. 8.19. Typical d.c. drive block diagram

The reference and the feedback signals are compared by the speed-loop amplifier and any error is amplified. Therefore if the motor speed falls below the desired speed, due for example to increased load, this error causes the phase angle to increase so as to increase the torque of the motor which will then cause the motor to accelerate to the desired speed.

The current loop and trigger module

It is essential that the armature current supplied by the thyristor controller be limited to a safe instantaneous value for the protection of both the thyristors and the motor. This is achieved by comparing the error signal from the speed amplifier with that of a current reference (Fig. 8.19). If this error exceeds the current reference then the phase angle is restricted so that the current through the armature is controlled to a safe limit. This feature, as shown by the diagram, can be extended to a variable current reference so that the torque control may be achieved. For normal thyristor controlled d.c. drives we may consider the system to be constant torque.

The output of the current amplifier is accepted by a trigger module whose function is to convert the error signal into a firing angle. The trigger module is synchronized with the supply so as to achieve a phase relationship for the firing pulse with respect to the supply.

Reversing module

The Electrocomp RA 37 reversing module is designed specifically to be used with the RMB (200 W) 50A and 50T (400 W) thyristor motor speed controllers (Figs. 8.20 and 8.21) for applications which call for a reversing duty or cycle. The unit ensures freedom from damage to the controller and blown fuses that may result from reversing the armature with the motor still revolving.

On selecting motor reversal, the reversal assembly switches off the motor control output and allows the driven system to run down at its natural rate. Once the system has come to rest, the armature connections are automatically reversed by a relay in the reversing assembly. The motor control unit then runs up the system under normal controlled acceleration. This method of control ensures smooth reversal and long relay life. Power is derived from the motor controller.

Connected to a controller through a 10 W terminal strip, the RA37 is simpler to install than alternative circuit arrangements, such as a pair of contactors and breaking resistor which need to be wired individually, resulting in increased costs and material.

The armature voltage feedback with load compensation gives a 50:1 speed range. This Electrocomp RMB 22A thyristor speed controller for d.c. motors up to 125 W has pre-settable potentiometers for maximum and minimum speeds with load compensation and current limiting.

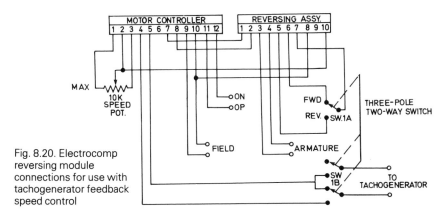

Fig. 8.20. Electrocomp reversing module connections for use with tachogenerator feedback speed control

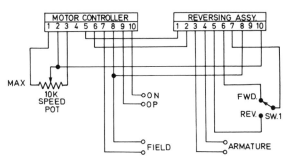

Fig. 8.21. Electrocomp reversing module connections for use with armature-voltage feedback speed control

9 Cranes and lifts

To a large extent the wiring circuits involved in the application of electrical equipment to the operation of cranes and lifts are similar in principle to those used to supply and control a.c. and d.c. motors driving other industrial machinery. Additional special circuits are needed to meet particular duty requirements.

The control scheme for crane motors depends on the type of motor used, the class of crane and its duty. Slow-speed low-lift cranes can be powered by a.c. motors and controlled from the floor by pendant-type pushbutton control stations. A high-speed high-lift overhead travelling crane will be powered by d.c. motors operated from a controller in the cab included in a complex scheme incorporating all the special features essential to safe operation. The controller may be a drum type directly switching the motor circuits, or a master type remotely controlling the operation of contactors.

Crane control schemes

Fig. 9.1 shows the basic control circuits of the d.c. series motors powering an overhead travelling crane. For this type of crane, d.c. series motors provide high starting torque, high speed and precise control. The first two circuits are for controlling long travel or cross traverse motions. The circuits include limit switches to prevent over-travel and a series-wound solenoid brake which is held off when the circuit is energized but applied by powerful spring action when the circuit is opened for any reason by the controller or by a limit switch or by supply failure.

As shown in Fig. 9.1, the hoist motion control circuit has particular features to ensure safe operation. The brake is a shunt-wound type so that it can still be energized to hold it off when lowering with the motor disconnected from the supply. The control scheme is such that when lowering, dynamic braking is provided on the first three notches. This is followed by a free position where the brake is held off and the load

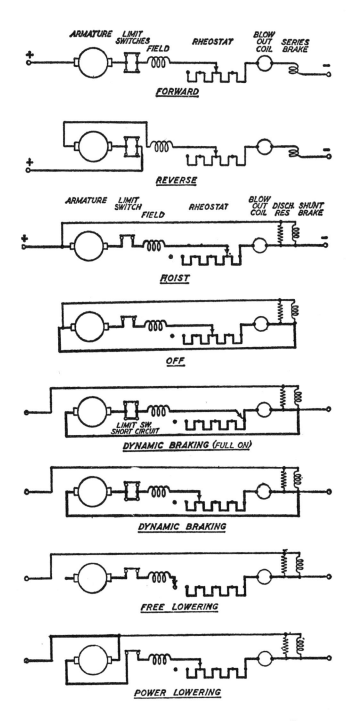

Fig. 9.1. Basic control circuits of d.c. series motors for overhead travelling crane

descends by gravity, and then the next two notches give power lowering for use when sending down an empty hook.

To obtain maximum hoisting and lowering speeds with precise control under all load conditions, the scheme shown in Fig. 9.2 is used. With this scheme, high speed operation can be achieved safely with both a light hook and the heaviest loads, and creep speeds can be minimized.

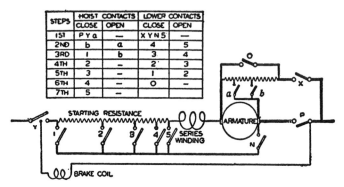

STEPS	HOIST CONTACTS		LOWER CONTACTS	
	CLOSE	OPEN	CLOSE	OPEN
1ST	P Y a	—	X Y N 5	—
2ND	b	a	4	5
3RD	1	b	3	4
4TH	2	—	2	3
5TH	3	—	1	2
6TH	4	—	0	—
7TH	5	—		

Fig. 9.2. Control circuits of d.c. series motor with starting resistor, slow-speed steps of armature divertor for hoisting, and potentiometer resistor for lowering

For certain duties, the a.c. three-phase commutator motor can be applied to crane drives. Various other schemes have been developed to enable induction motors to be applied to meet particular handling requirements and especially to provide a stable creep speed irrespective of the load on the hook and the direction of motion.

Passenger lift control systems

Distinctive features of passenger lift circuits are the various safety devices incorporated to guard against failures of equipment and any attempts to operate or utilize the lift in a dangerous manner, e.g. to open gates when the car is in motion. Comprehensive interlocking schemes are necessary to ensure that the lift motor cannot be energized unless each of several pairs of contacts in series is closed. Because this interlocking is of critical importance it is essential for the wiring to be carried out correctly, otherwise the interlocking may not provide the safeguard intended and may in fact be a potential cause of accidents due to inadvertent mal-operation of the lift. Fig. 9.3 shows typical interlocking schemes for lifts operating from different forms of supply.

The main electrical components of a passenger lift are represented in Fig. 9.4 together with other items involved in the control scheme. Most of the features shown are included in all three schemes illustrated by Figs. 9.5, 9.6 and 9.8, but which differ in certain other respects.

Considering the features common to all three schemes, the motor is a type which is started, stopped and reversed by the operation of contactors controlled in two of the schemes by a car-switch and in the third, automatic, scheme by car and landing pushbuttons. The motor is also

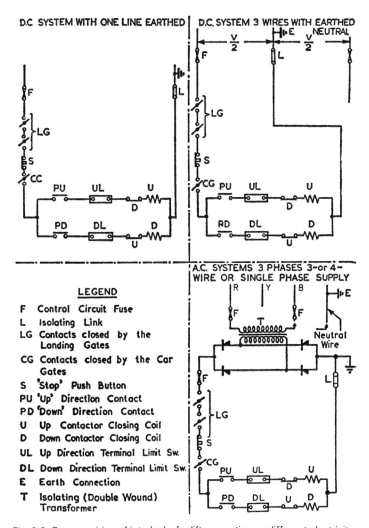

Fig. 9.3. Correct wiring of interlocks for lifts operating on different electricity supplies

equipped with an electromagnetic brake which is applied automatically when the motor is switched off normally or by the action of a limit switch or other protective device.

The stopping limit switches stop the car at terminal landings despite continued operation of the car switch or pushbuttons, but a safeguard against the failure of a stopping limit switch is provided by the overtravel limit switches which stop the car if it passes the normal limits of travel. The car safety operated switch stops the motor in the event of the car safety mechanism being applied. The overspeed governor causes the car safety mechanism to be applied if the descending car speed exceeds a predetermined value.

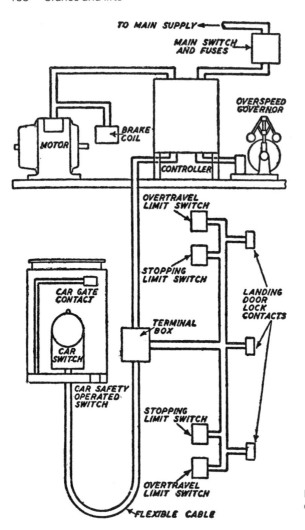

Fig. 9.4. Components of car-switch-operated d.c. lift

Additional protective devices are the car-gate contact which ensures that the gate must be closed before the lift will work and that it will remain closed while the lift is working; and the landing-door locks which prevent a door being opened unless the car is opposite to that door, and which ensure that the lift will not work unless all the landing doors are closed.

Fig. 9.5 shows the wiring circuits for a single-speed car-switch-operated d.c. lift. The contactors are in the 'off' position with the lift at rest and all landing doors and the car gate closed. At starting, the circuit through the various switches is energized from the positive of the supply up to the car switch in the 'off' position. When the car switch handle is moved to the 'up' position this completes a circuit to the negative line through the 'up' contacts, coil A of the 'up' reversing contactor, interlock contacts b6 and auxiliary contacts d5 of the accelerating switch. Thus the 'up' reversing contactor operating coil is energized and the main making contacts A1 and A2 close and the main breaking contacts A3 open.

When contacts A1 close, auxiliary contacts a5 close to operate the main contactor which closes contacts C1 and C2 to complete a circuit from the positive to the negative line through the closed contacts A1 and B3, the armature and A2 contacts, the starting resistor and the series field winding. The shunt field winding is energized by the closing of contacts C1, A1 and C2, and the brake is taken off by its coil being energized through the closed contacts C1, A1, a4, C3, C4 and C2.

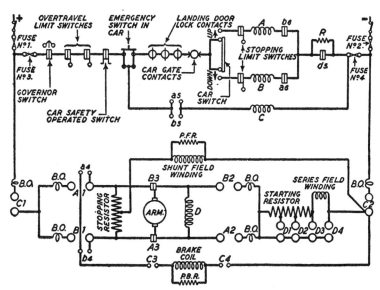

Fig. 9.5. Circuits of single-speed car-switch-operated d.c. lift. Items identified by 'A' are related to the 'up' reversing contactor; by 'B', to the 'down' reversing contactor; by 'C', to the main contactor; by 'D', to the accelerating switch. B.O. indicates the contactor blow-out coils

As the armature accelerates, the voltage across coil D of the accelerating switch increases and the switch contacts D1–D4 close successively to short-circuit the starting resistor and finally the series winding.

When the car-switch is moved to the 'down' position the sequence of operations is similar excepting that the 'down' reversing contactor operates to close contacts B1 and B2 and open contacts B3 to reverse the direction of rotation of the motor.

Moving the car-switch to the 'off' position to stop the lift opens the appropriate reversing contactor and the main contactor, the brake is applied and at the same time the motor is braked dynamically by the closing of contacts A3 and B3 to connect the stopping resistor across the armature.

Fig. 9.6 shows a scheme with an a.c. motor but with d.c. control circuits supplied through rectifiers. The control scheme is similar to that shown in Fig. 9.5. Subject to the protective circuits being normal, when the coil A of the 'up' reversing contactor is energized, contacts a3 close to energize the main contactor which closes contacts C1 and C2 to complete the circuit from the main switch through contacts A1 and A2 to the starting resistor and the motor stator winding. The brake-coil circuit is completed by contacts c3 and energized from No. 2 rectifier when C1 and C2 close to connect it to the supply. The coil D of the accelerating contactor is also energized from No. 2 rectifier and operates the contactor which closes contacts D1–D3 to short-circuit the starting resistors.

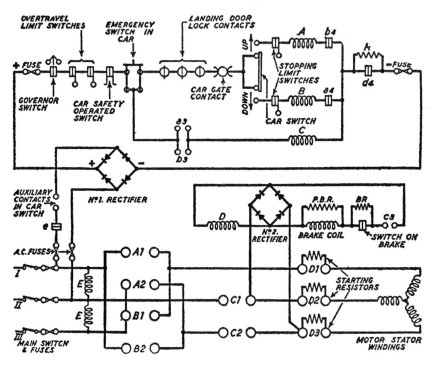

Fig. 9.6. Circuits of single-speed car-switch-operated lift with induction motor drive and d.c. control circuits supplied through rectifiers. Items identified by 'A' are related to the 'up' reversing contactor; by 'B', to the 'down' reversing contactor; by 'C', to the main contactor; by 'D' to the accelerating contactor. E indicates the phase-failure relay.

When the car-switch is moved to the 'down' position, the reversing contactor B operates to close contacts B1 and B2 and change over the connections of the motor to the supply to reverse its direction of rotation.

Fig. 9.7 shows the schematic arrangement of the components of an automatic d.c. passenger lift and Fig. 9.8 shows the circuits. The control scheme is similar to that shown in Fig. 9.5 but is designed to incorporate the car and landing pushbutton controls. The floor controller enables the car to be called or dispatched to any particular floor, and the car pushbuttons enable the car to be dispatched to the floor required and stopped in emergency. In conjuction with a relay, when the car is occupied the floor switch makes the landing pushbuttons ineffective, prevents the

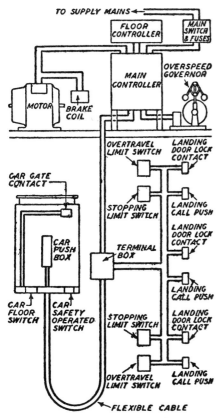

TO SUPPLY MAINS

FLOOR CONTROLLER

MAIN SWITCH & FUSES

MAIN CONTROLLER

OVERSPEED GOVERNOR

MOTOR

BRAKE COIL

OVERTRAVEL LIMIT SWITCH

LANDING DOOR LOCK CONTACT

CAR GATE CONTACT

STOPPING LIMIT SWITCH

LANDING CALL PUSH

LANDING DOOR LOCK CONTACT

CAR PUSH BOX

TERMINAL BOX

LANDING CALL PUSH

CAR FLOOR SWITCH

CAR SAFETY OPERATED SWITCH

STOPPING LIMIT SWITCH

LANDING DOOR LOCK CONTACT

OVERTRAVEL LIMIT SWITCH

LANDING CALL PUSH

FLEXIBLE CABLE

Fig. 9.7. Components of automatic d.c. lift

operation of the lift unless the car gate is closed, and completes the circuit for the car pushbutton control.

Refer now to Fig. 9.8 and assume that the car is at floor 1 and is called to floor 2. The circuit is already made through various closed contacts up to the common connection of the landing pushes, and pressing No. 2 landing push completes the circuit from the positive to the negative line through coil G2 of the floor controller relay and the 'up' limit switch, interlock contacts b6, coil A of the 'up' reversing contactor, the 'up' stopping limit switch and the contacts d5.

The motor connections are then made by switching operations which are the same as those for the scheme shown in Fig. 9.5, except that the circuit does not include a main contactor and its contacts C. When the coil of relay G2 is energized its contacts g2 close so that the relay and the 'up' reversing contactor are held closed until the car arrives at floor 2. It will be noted that, if the car is already occupied when a landing push is pressed, this action has no effect since the circuit to the common landing push connection is opened by the depression of the car floor switch.

When an empty car is called by a landing push, as it starts the car push circuit contacts a5 open and contacts a7 close to complete the circuit for the time relay F and its contacts f open the landing push circuit, so that a call from another landing is not effective. As the car approaches floor 2 the 'up' floor controller limits switch is opened so that the holding coils of the relay G2 and the contactor A are de-energized. Contacts a7 open to de-energize relay F but the reclosing of its contacts f (in circuit to the landing pushes) is delayed to enable the landing door to be opened before the car can be called to another floor.

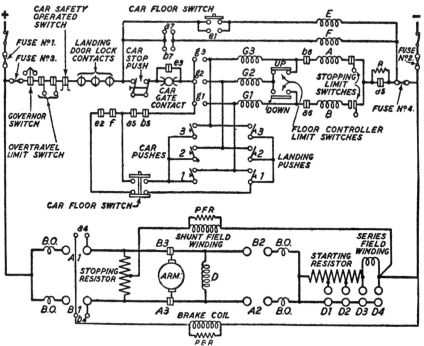

Fig. 9.8. Circuits of automatic pushbutton-operated d.c. lift. Items identified by 'A' are related to the 'up' reversing contactor; by 'B', to the 'down' reversing contactor; by 'D' to the accelerating switch; by 'E', to the car-holding relay; by 'F', to the timing relay; by 'G', to the floor relays

An emergency stop is made from the car by pressing the 'stop' push and the normal protective devices are also effective. Opening of a reversing contactor switches off the motor, applies the brake and connects the dynamic braking resistor.

With pushbutton control from the car, the circuit to the car push common connection is made when the car-floor switch is depressed by the entry of the passenger. This switch also opens the landing push circuit. As soon as the landing door is closed the coil of the car-holding relay E is energized and it closes contacts e1 to short-circuit the appropriate contacts of the car-floor switch to provide a holding circuit for the relay until a landing door is opened.

Assuming that the car is at floor 1 and the push for floor 2 is pressed, the circuit is made through the coil of relay G2 and the 'up' reversing contactor coil A so that the relay and the contactor are energized and held closed as when the car is called from a landing push. If the car is standing at floor 3 and the floor 2 push is pressed, the control circuit is made through the coil of relay G2, the 'down' limit switch of the floor controller to the coil of the 'down' reversing contactor B. The motor circuits are then switched in a sequence similar to that for the scheme shown in Fig. 9.5. Fig. 9.9 shows a complete circuit of a two-floor single-speed lift.

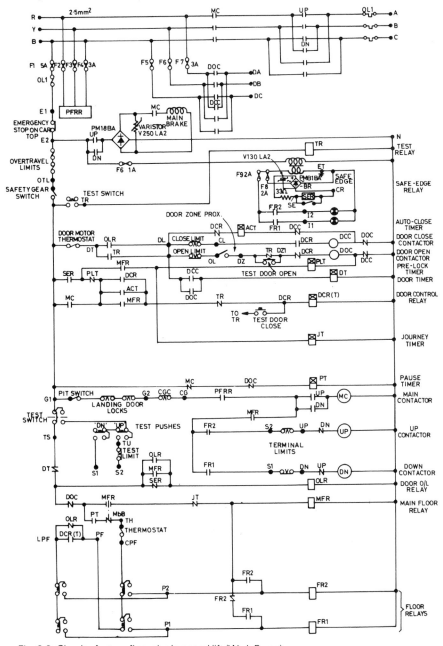

Fig. 9.9. Circuit of a two-floor single-speed lift (W. J. Furse)

10 Welding circuits

The variety of welding processes can be classified as either 'arc' or 'resistance', according to whether the welding heat is derived from an arc between an electrode and the workpiece or results from the passage of a heavy current through two metal surfaces in contact under pressure.

Arc-welding processes

Several arc-welding processes are available for different applications. For general-purpose welding and fabrication there is the manual (metal arc) process using consumable stick electrodes.

Employed with both semi-automatic and automatic set-ups, the basic MIG (metal inert gas) process has a consumable electrode in the form of a continuous wire fed on to the workpiece at a constant preset rate. The arc is shielded by carbon dioxide (CO_2). There are several versions of the MIG process, each suitable for particular ranges of metals and/or classes of work.

Using argon gas to shield an arc struck between a non-consumable tungsten electrode and the workpiece, the Argonarc TIG (tungsten inert gas) process was developed for the special-purpose welding of mild and stainless steel, aluminium and light alloys.

Instead of a gas shield the automatic submerged arc process keeps the arc submerged in a trail of powdered flux, the bare wire electrode (or electrodes) being fed to the workpiece at a controlled rate. Where applicable, this process gives high speeds on thin plate and high deposition rates on heavy plate.

Also in the arc-welding category is the process using a consumable flux-coated electrode, and the two electro-slag processes that are generally suitable for structural and other heavy work.

Power supply units

The effective utilization of each particular process depends on providing the appropriate power supply unit. With some processes either an a.c. or a d.c. supply may be used but the power unit must be designed to give a drooping volt/ampere characteristic. Other processes require a d.c. source with a flat characteristic while for certain processes the supply requirement is not critical and any one of several power units may be used if the current output and control range are sufficient for the purpose.

The simplest source of welding power is the single-operator a.c. welding unit which consists essentially of a transformer and a regulator. Fig. 10.1 shows the circuits of a Murex single-operator transformer unit with a continuous rating of 12 kVA and an intermittent hand welding rating of 26.6 kVA. It provides a current range of 16–333 A at 80 V and 20–265 A at 100 V. The unit is one of a range of four the largest of which has a continuous rating of 16.8 kVA.

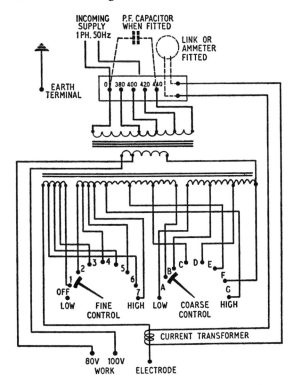

Fig. 10.1. Single-operator transformer welding unit

The double-wound transformer is oil-cooled. Current control is obtained by means of a tapped-type reactor and a rotary selector switch provides a choice from seven ranges. Fine adjustment over each range is obtained by a seven-way-and-off selector switch. The combination of both switches gives 49 adjustments on 80 V and 47 on 100 V, a total of 96 settings. The steps are graduated to give fine adjustments at low currents and coarser adjustments at higher currents.

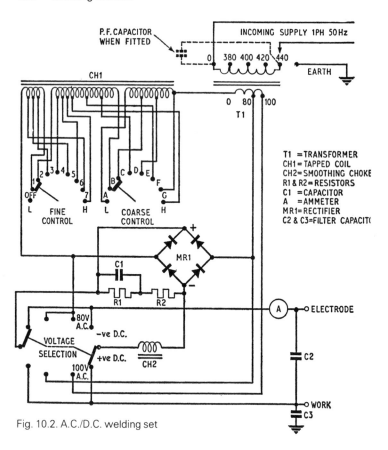

Fig. 10.2. A.C./D.C. welding set

A similar control scheme is the welding set shown in Fig. 10.2 to regulate the output of the transformer to the a.c. terminals and to the silicon diode rectifier. With the smaller of two units available, the a.c. range is 16–333 A at 80 V open-circuit and 20–265 A at 100 V open-circuit, and the d.c. range is 13–250 A at 70 V open-circuit. A switch selects either a.c. or d.c. and with each the current can be adjusted over 49 settings by operating two other switches. This type of unit can be used for metal arc and Argonarc processes.

Welding sets can be designed for use by more than one operator. Fig. 10.3 shows the main circuits of a three-phase equipment supplying three arcs, each controlled by a separate regulator.

A d.c. generator is used for welding either because it provides the characteristic essential for a particular process or when an a.c. supply is not available and the power must necessarily be obtained from an engine-driven unit. When the welding requirement determines the specific use of a d.c. generator, it may be driven by an a.c. motor.

Developed by Lincoln Electric Co. Ltd., the fully automatic Lincoln-weld submerged-arc process uses bare electrode wire which is fed into a blanket of granular flux deposited on the joint to be welded at a depth

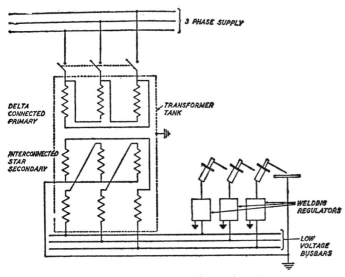

Fig. 10.3. Three-phase multi-operator welding equipment

sufficient to cover the weld metal. The rate of wire feed is controlled automatically to maintain the correct arc length. A d.c. supply is derived from a Lincoln motor-generator set.

The power and control circuits are shown in Figs. 10.4 and 10.5. The scheme provides for the control of arc voltage and welding current, the wire feed motor and, with one type of unit, the motor driving the welding head carriage which is used for jobs where the work remains stationary and the welding head travels.

With the control circuits shown in Fig. 10.5, the required constant arc length is maintained by the related action of the 35 V control exciter, the wire feed motor armature voltage and the arc voltage. The wire feed motor and the control exciter are in series with each other and in parallel with the arc voltage. The wire feed motor voltage is the difference between the arc voltage and the control exciter voltage, which is set at some constant value by the arc volts rheostat.

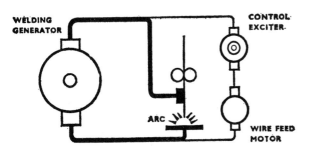

Fig. 10.4. Main circuits of Lincolnweld system

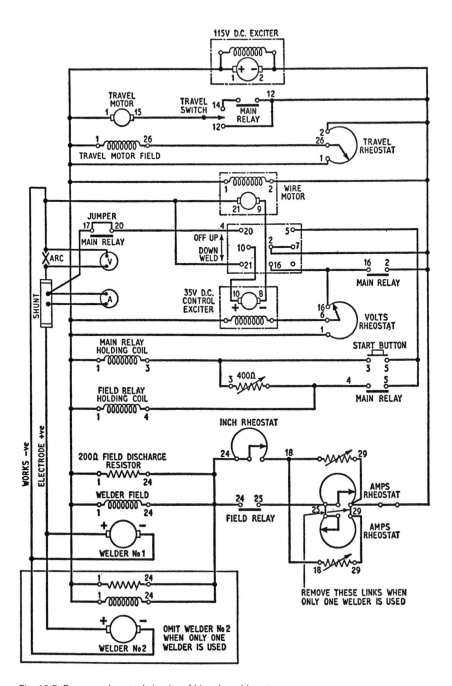

Fig. 10.5. Power and control circuits of Lincolnweld system

If for any reason (such as a depression in the work) the arc length increases, the wire feed motor voltage increases momentarily since it is in parallel with the arc voltage, which varies directly with the length of the arc. The increasing voltage speeds up the wire feed and brings the arc length back to its original value, while a decreasing voltage slows down the wire feed. Since the arc length is proportional to the arc voltage, and the value of the arc voltage is controlled with the control exciter (arc volts) setting, this is the factor determining the arc length.

The power for inching the wire up is provided by the 35 V control exciter, and the power for inching down by the welding generator. Before beginning the welding operation, the wire is inched down to the work and when the start button is pressed, the wire is retracted automatically by inching and the arc is struck. The wire is inched up because the control exciter voltage is directly across the wire feed motor armature. The wire continues to inch up until the arc voltage exceeds the control exciter voltage. When the two are equal, there is no further movement of the wire. As the wire melts down, the arc voltage will exceed the control exciter voltage so that the wire will be inched down until the two voltages are again equal.

A potentiometer circuit is used for voltage control of the 35 V exciter in order to vary the voltage across the field from 0–115 V without opening the field circuit.

Resistance welding techniques

The four basic resistance welding techniques are: spot welding, including stitch welding; projection welding; seam welding; butt and flash-butt welding. The equipments for these techniques comprise three units: the transformer and electrode assembly; the mechanism for applying the weld pressure; and the timer controlling the length of time of welding current flow. These units differ according to the technique involved.

As shown in Fig. 10.6 the a.c. supply is applied to the primary winding of the transformer through a contactor which is controlled by the timer. The transformer steps down the input to a low voltage heavy current the value of which can be adjusted by selection of the tappings of the primary windings. The welding current is conveyed to the workpiece through the copper electrodes, the lower one being normally fixed and the upper one moveable in a vertical plane. With light duty machines a foot-pedal lever-operated system (Fig. 10.7) may be used to apply weld pressure but most modern machines are operated by compressed air.

Machines for stitch and projection welding are similar in principle to the spot welder. Stitch welding consists of a series of overlapped spot welds and with projection welding projections or embossments are raised on the work-piece to form the welded zone.

The arrangement of a seam welding machine is shown in Fig. 10.8. It makes a number of spot welds by means of rotating copper-alloy wheel electrodes without the electrodes opening between spots. The electrode wheel applies a constant force to the workpiece and rotates at controlled speeds. The spot welding is effected by on/off switching of the primary

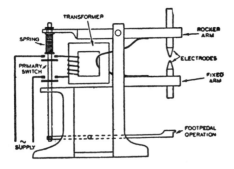

Fig. 10.6. Schematic circuit of spot-welding machine. The current is concentrated at the lap joint by means of electrode tips of limited area. A development of spot welding is projection welding, in which a number of welds may be made simultaneously by flat electrodes, the current being concentrated by projections on one or both of the components

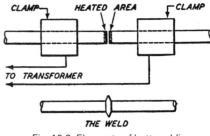

Fig. 10.7. Basic circuits of pedal-operated spot welder

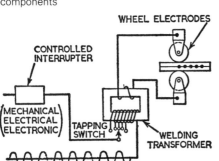

Fig. 10.8. Arrangement of seam-welding machine. The work passes between two roller electrodes while the current flows continuously or intermittently, producing a line of overlapping or individual spots

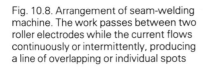

Fig. 10.9. Elements of butt-welding machine. With normal butt welding the two ends are brought together before the current is switched on. With flash-butt welding the two ends are brought close enough to start an arc to heat the areas shown in the diagram before the ends are pushed together

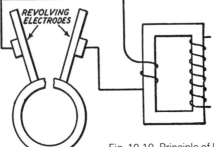

Fig. 10.10. Principle of butt seam welding

current to produce intermittent secondary current pulses through the workpiece. The current pulses may be timed to produce either overlapping or separate spots.

The elements of a butt welding machine are shown in Fig. 10.9. The parts to be joined are held in clamps and a heavy low-voltage current is passed through them from the secondary winding of the transformer. Initially, the ends are brought together at a reduced pressure while the current is passed through the joint to heat it up, and the pressure is high enough to prevent flashing. At a predetermined point, the pressure is increased to forge the weld and then the current is switched off. The clamps are mounted on platens one of which is movable to apply the initial and final pressures.

The difference between butt and flash-butt welding is that with the latter the parts to be joined are initially kept far enough apart to produce an arc between them. The heat generated by the arc raises the temperature at the ends to near melting point and then the current is switched off and the ends pushed together to form the weld.

Fig. 10.10 shows the principle of butt seam welding which is used for the continuous welding of tube joints. The electrodes are in the form of wheels revolving along the length of the tube while pressure is applied to the joint.

Resistance welding control circuits

To produce high quality resistance welds several factors have to be precisely controlled. One requirement is that the welding current must be maintained at the correct value and a second is that the welding time must be constant. Automatic control equipment is necessary to ensure that these requirements are met, and with modern machines high performance is achieved by the use of electronic schemes. In general, the schemes are either non-synchronous or synchronous.

With non-synchronous control the welding current may start and finish at any point in the supply waveform, depending on the instant at which control is initiated. A non-synchronous timer can be used to energize a contactor which switches the supply to the primary winding of the welder transformer during the weld time. This class of control is used for fairly long weld times of the order of 0.2 second (10 cycles) or more, with transformer primary currents of less than 300 A, and when the weld repetition rate is low and the workpiece material will not be affected by some variation in the weld heat.

Fig. 10.11 shows the circuits of a thyristor contactor non-synchronous timer for a spot welder. It allows the welding current to flow for a predetermined time, the value of the welding current being set by selecting taps on the transformer. On/off switching of the supply is by the welding contactor the closing coil of which is energized when the thyristor is conducting. The weld time depends on the period when the thyristor is conducting.

To initiate a weld, a circuit is made between terminals 1 and 2 to energize relay 3. The capacitor 4 is then switched into the gate circuit of the thyristor to make its grid positive so that it conducts and energizes the

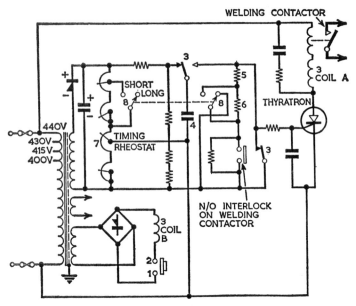

Fig. 10.11. Non-synchronous contactor timer

contactor coil. The capacitor then discharges through resistors 5 and 6 so that after a certain time the grid becomes negative with respect to the cathode, the thyristor stops conducting and the contactor opens to switch off the welding current. The welding time is adjusted by means of the rheostat 7. The control scheme provides for two timing ranges; a short range of 5–100 cycles, and a long range of 1–10 seconds.

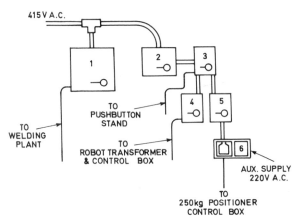

Fig. 10.12. Typical power requirements for a robot welding system. (1) 45 A switch-fuse for welding supply. (2) 30 A switch-fuse for robot and auxiliary line socket-outlets. (3) 30 A contactor to control supply to robot and work positioner. (4), (5) 20 A fused isolators. (6) Dual-gang socket-outlet

Robot welding

Here the addition to the welding unit is a robot manipulator and controller. Typical power requirements for a Lansing Industrial Welding Robot are shown in Fig. 10.12. It will be necessary to mount the workpiece so that it can be operated by the programmer. For some applications a triple-headed positioner may be required. Heavier jobs may need a multi-axis turntable. An indexing microprocessor operates during the welding cycle.

When welding is completed, the positioner indexes to present the newly loaded components to the robot for welding while the operator unloads the finished assembly and loads a new set of components. For correct welding robot operation, careful planning between the robot supplier and customer is essential.

11 Energy control management systems

Energy management refers to schemes for eliminating waste in the use of electricity. The current trend is towards a rise in the cost of electrical energy. For this reason various electrical engineering methods, some of which are set out below, have been devised with the objective of reducing wastage in electricity and making it more competitive with other fuels.

Energy management principles

The Square D Ltd scheme follows the basic rule that any facility with a large monthly electric bill is a candidate for an energy management system. The other criterion is that the facility has loads that can be turned off for short periods without adversely affecting productivity or comfort. Examples of such loads are air conditioning, ventilating and exhaust fans, electric and water heaters, and battery chargers.

Most commercial and industrial electricity tariffs are made up of two charges – energy usage and maximum demand. The energy charge is based on the quantity of electricity consumed, while the demand charge is based on the peak amount of energy used during the charging period. Both these charges should be controlled to keep the electricity bill at its lowest practical level.

After a demand limit has been set (Fig. 11.1(a)) the energy management system will monitor the facility demand and then shed controllable loads when the demand approaches the limit.

Savings can also be made on demand and energy by cycling loads (Fig. 11.1(b)). With variations in the starting time to begin cycling each load, a staggered pattern will limit the number of loads allowed on line. Again, by varying the 'on' time and 'off' time for each load (1–90 minutes), virtually any duty cycling pattern may be selected.

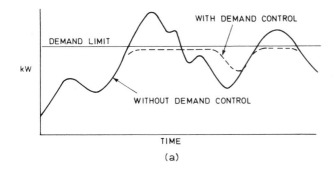

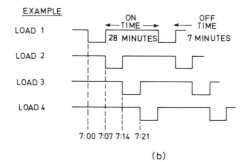

Fig. 11.1. (a) Load demand control.
(b) Load cycling; after a power outage
all cycling loads automatically return to
the staggered pattern

Cadam systems structure

Here, microprocessor technology is employed to ensure minimum energy consumption by means of the units shown in the block diagram of Fig. 11.2. For *heating*, an optimum start system enables the building temperature to be maintained only during hours of occupancy. It starts the heating as late as possible each morning so that an acceptable temperature is reached as people arrive. The system takes into account the temperature both inside and outside the building, so allowance is made, for example, for a cold Monday morning. The control is self-adaptive and tunes itself to a particular building. Close and continuous control over the temperatures within the building are essential for maximum economy. Just 1°C over the required temperature level may mean 10 per cent on the fuel bill. This system uses solid-state sensors in place of thermostats.

The optimum start and temperature control also applies to *air conditioning*. In addition, the intake of fresh air is controlled to make good use of any 'free' cooling that can be produced during the spring and autumn when the outside air may be nearer the required temperature than the actual recirculated air within the building. When heat is required, the control system closes the fresh-air dampers during the warm-up period and before the arrival of personnel. This eliminates heat wastage through the air conditioning system prior to occupation.

Lighting can be controlled too, the lights being automatically turned off outside occupation hours. Illumination-level control can also be used. A reduction in maintenance costs is effected by monitoring the hours run for each plant unit and advising when maintenance is required.

176

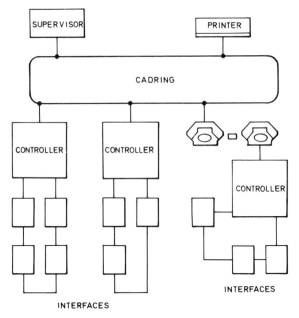

Fig. 11.2. Block diagram of Holec Cadam control system

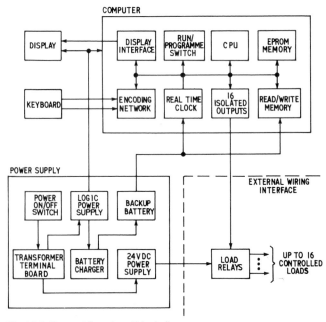

Fig. 11.3. Enertrol functional block diagram

Operating programming

The Enertrol energy management system follows similar lines. The block diagram for this appears as Fig. 11.3. To reduce energy charges, programming is carried out by an operator. A ventilating system with a number of supply fans can have several units shut down on a rotating basis for a few minutes at a time without noticeably affecting the comfort level.

Duomax

The Landis and Gyr system monitors the electrical energy consumed during every integrating period and, by disconnecting sheddable loads, prevents the preselected target load being exceeded. It also gives the command to reconnect the loads as soon as is permissible.

A typical Duomax monitoring system is illustrated in Fig. 11.4. The load impulses from the electricity meter 2 and the timing signal from the time switch 1 are transmitted to the Duomax controller, via the interposing relays 3 and 4, and processed. The controller automatically monitors the pre-set load target and controls the disconnecting and connecting of the sheddable loads.

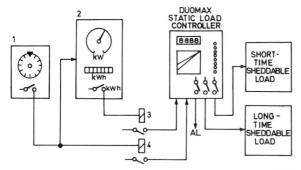

Fig. 11.4. Block diagram of a Duomax monitoring system. (1) Time switch with transmitting contact. (2) Electricity meter with transmitting contact and maximum-demand indicator. (3), (4) Interposing relays. (AL) Output for signalling collective alarm

The Duomax can be adjusted on site to suit the value of the impulse transmitted from the electricity meter and the appropriate integrating period T_m (Fig. 11.5), the target load P_m that must not be exceeded in the integrating period, and the load conditions. The loads can be divided into the following groups: base load P1, which should not be switched off (i.e. motors, lifts, minimum lighting); load L1, which can be disconnected for a short time during the integrating period (i.e. heating stages of boilers and ovens); and load L2, which can be disconnected for a longer time during the integrating period (e.g. heating retaining stages of boilers and ovens, and heating and cooling stages of air-conditioning systems).

As an example of an integrating period (using the nomenclature of Fig. 11.5) the following events take place. At the beginning of the integrating period (A) all loads (P1, L1, L2) are switched in. At time point B the Duomax gives the order to disconnect load L2. At time point C, another

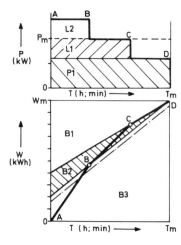

Fig. 11.5. Description, and example, of an integrating period

order is given, this time to disconnect load L1. From C to D (end of the integrating period) only the base load P1 is switched in.

The consumption diagram shows the pre-set load ranges and the actual course of the consumption during the integrating period in three stages. (1) At the beginning of the consumption period (A) the consumption is in the range B3; all loads can be switched in. (2) When the consumption reaches the division between ranges B3 and B2 (time point B), the load L2 can be disconnected. (3) When the consumption reaches the dividing line between B2 and the range B1, the load L1 is disconnected (time point C).

Response control system

A response control system has been developed by MK Electric Ltd. It is not only a method of operating electrical apparatus by remote control but also makes for energy conservation by its ability to programme in advance when certain lights are turned off rather than allow their random use.

The heart of the system is the mains controller (Fig. 11.6) which is a microprocessor-based desktop unit providing both programmable as well as manual switching of remote appliances. The most significant feature of the system is that it uses the existing mains wiring as the transmission channel for the control signals.

Response uses a two-way communication system that continuously monitors the on/off state of the electrical appliances and equipment controlled by the system. Pulse-coded signals are sent from the controller to each response accessory (up to 32 can be used). These accessories contain microelectronic circuitry to decode and react to the signals transmitted over the mains wiring. Each unit has a current rating of 13 A and contains both an indicator light and a pushbutton override switch. These accessories can be obtained in two forms – a plug-in adaptor for controlling these items normally connected via sockets, and a junction box for the control of individual circuits or hard-wired appliances. Loads greater than 13 A can be switched by using a contactor together with the

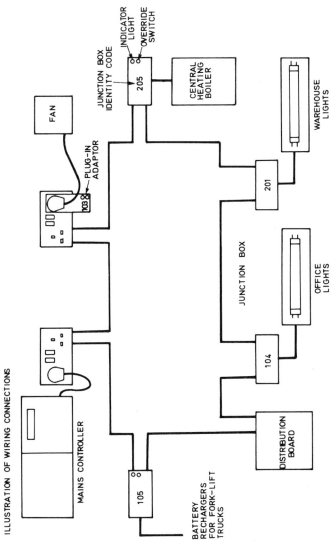

Fig. 11.6. Response-control system

response junction box. The junction box also has two additional terminals so that when it is mounted, for example, in a ceiling void a remote override switch can be wired into a convenient point.

In order to provide full switching flexibility there is an additional switch unit (called a zone controller) which has four pushbutton switches, each of which can be programmed to switch on or off individual or groups of junction boxes or adapters independently of the main controller.

In common with other systems, individual switching instructions can be programmed into the controller in advance to take effect either at a regular time every day or on specified days of the week. In this way heating equipment can be programmed to come on either at the same time every day of the week or at different times on certain days, according to the usage of the building. The programming and switching systems have been designed so that the user can ensure that the equipment controlled is switched on only when required, i.e. office lighting is turned off at lunch time and again when staff leave at the end of the day, and heating systems are only working when the area is occupied.

Lighting

Since the cost of electric lighting now forms a large proportion of the energy bill, many schemes now concentrate solely on this aspect. Savings may easily be made by fitting miniature fluorescent lamps. These are claimed to give five times longer lamp life with six times greater efficiency, resulting in savings up to 80 per cent of energy plus a saving in replacement costs. Elkay Electrical Manufacturing Ltd cite consumption comparisons with filament lamps as follows:

Type	PL9	SL9	SL13	SL18	2D
Fluorescent	9 W	9 W	13 W	13 W	21 W
Filament	60 W	40 W	60 W	75 W	100 W

These tubes are fitted into modern-type luminaires. The longer straight fluorescent tubes with the slimmer 25 mm diameter with krypton gas filling and an inner coating of tryphosphor, also make for increased efficiency.

By use of the Energy Conservation System (ECS), fluorescent, tungsten and discharge lighting may be controlled on a local or zone basis by time and daylight linking. ECS main pulse interrupt reset devices operate on the principle of automatically reverting to the 'off' state whenever the mains supply to the reset switch unit is interrupted for one second. These units have shown savings of 40 per cent.

Energy management by infra-red and ripple control

The Home Automation Ltd system enables energy management of lighting of new or existing buildings using existing luminaires and (similar to the MK system) existing wiring.

Local control responds to the need of each individual unit on the spot. As shown in Fig. 11.7, master controllers may be added to each luminaire or group of luminaires. The functions of these master controllers may be 'switching' or 'switching + time lag off + photocell' or 'dimming' or 'photocell dimming' (constant brightness) control.

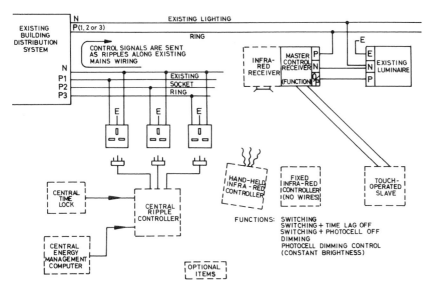

Fig. 11.7. Block diagram for lighting energy-management system

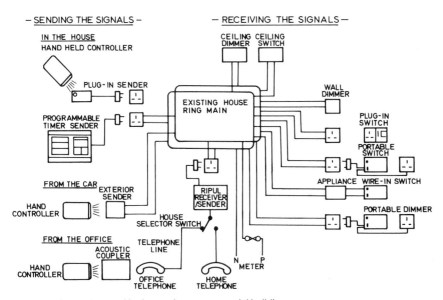

Fig. 11.8. General control in domestic or commercial buildings

Slave control of the master may be made from (a) hand-held remote-control transmitter, (b) surface-mounted remote-control transmitter, (c) wall-mounted slave touch plate using the existing wiring from the old system, or (d) central programmer which needs a mains supply but no other wiring. The remote-control transmitters send infra-red signals which are received by the master controller. The transmitters send either simple pulses for control of a single-channel system or pulse-code modulated signals if multiple-channel control is desired. Energy may be saved in four ways. (a) Lights are only switched on by demand from individuals. (b) Lights are switched by a photocell detecting excessive ambient light in the neighbourhood of the master controller. (c) Lights are turned off after expiry of a time-lag period. (d) Lights are turned off from the central programmer.

Fig. 11.8 illustrates the general use from which many applications may be derived. As described, signals may be transmitted in various ways. Typically a hand-held controller can be used to send signals to receivers which, in turn, may perform simple switching functions or more complex functions such as dimming.

The use of infra-red signals from a hand-held transmitter to a receiver/sender, or the use of a sender to superimpose ripple signals on the existing mains wiring, or the use of a telephone line, are purely means of transmission. In all cases the nature of the signal is the same in that it contains the same pulse-code modulated data.

Index